iron

THE REPAIR OF WROUGHT AND CAST IRONWORK

Comhshaol, Oidhreacht agus Rialtas Áitiúil
Environment, Heritage and Local Government

DUBLIN
PUBLISHED BY THE STATIONERY OFFICE
To be purchased directly from:
Government Publications Sales Office
Sun Alliance House
Molesworth Street
Dublin 2

or by mail order from:
Government Publications
Postal Trade Section
Unit 20 Lakeside Retail Park
Claremorris
Co. Mayo

Tel: 01 – 6476834/37 or 1890 213434; Fax: 01 – 6476843 or 094 - 9378964
or through any bookseller

Text by: Ali Davey
Contributor: David Mitchell
Series Editor: Jacqui Donnelly

Copy Editor: Eleanor Flegg
Design: Bennis Design

Contents

Introduction

Ireland has a wonderfully rich heritage of historic ironwork. The extraordinary variety of the ironwork that survives around the country is testimony to the durability and functionality of the material. To this day, many streets are served by historic cast iron lamp standards and post-boxes. The strength and flexibility of iron made it a popular material for the construction of industrial buildings and glasshouses. From the capital's iconic Ha'penny Bridge, to the many terraces and squares bounded by iron railings and adorned with balconies and finials, the distinctive character of the country's towns and cities owes much to their legacy of ironwork.

Historic ironwork reflects not only the fashions and design trends of the eighteenth and nineteenth centuries. It is also the product of the skill and sweat of generations of men, women, and children who worked in the industry. The plain wrought iron railings that survive around so many Irish houses are the result of an incredible amount of labour; from the 'rabbler' who stood in the scorching heat to stir the wrought iron as

it bubbled in the furnace, to the hours spent by blacksmiths hammering at their anvils. Although mass-produced, cast ironwork also required great skill and back-breaking labour to make. Foundry men's days were spent working in the burning temperatures of the furnace workshops, hunched for hours over moulding boxes or carrying weighty crucibles laden with molten iron.

Nothing will remain in perfect condition forever if it is not cared for and maintained regularly. A simple regime of repainting once every five years, and touching up smaller areas of paint loss in the intervening period, will do much to prolong the life of historic ironwork. There are many cleaning and repair techniques that can be used to repair corroded or damaged cast and wrought ironwork. Even when ironwork may appear at first glance to be irredeemably corroded or damaged, it is often perfectly possible to repair. Corrosion often looks far worse than it actually is.

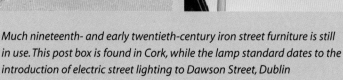

Cast iron railings and gate, Limerick

Much nineteenth- and early twentieth-century iron street furniture is still in use. This post box is found in Cork, while the lamp standard dates to the introduction of electric street lighting to Dawson Street, Dublin

Historic iron is renowned for its corrosion resistance and is generally an incredibly durable material. Much of the ironwork found in Ireland is over 100 years old and in some cases even older. Historic ironwork has a distinctive character that is rarely matched by modern replicas. Traditionally, blacksmiths and founders served long apprenticeships to hone their skills and, as a result, historic ironwork is usually of high quality.

The same cannot always be said for mild steel, the most common substitute material for the repair and replication of historic wrought and cast iron. It has an inferior resistance to corrosion so that mild steel replicas and repairs are more likely to corrode at a faster rate than the original ironwork they are replacing or repairing. Mild steel replicas are all too often made by fabricators (a term that is much confused with the term 'blacksmith') who usually do not have a knowledge or understanding of traditional blacksmithing. The result is a poor quality of design that has none of the detailing that gives traditional ironwork its character and visual appeal. Ultimately such a product is more likely to detract from, rather than enhance, the character of the historic building it adjoins or is part of. It therefore makes sense to repair and retain historic ironwork wherever possible. It is more durable than modern alternative materials and has been made with a level of skill that is rarely matched today.

This is a rare example of superb late eighteenth-century wrought ironwork. This highly ornate arch required considerable skill to make

An early and unusual multiple-wire cable suspension bridge (1826) in the grounds of Birr Castle, County Offaly

Conservation principles

In a sense, we look after our historic buildings for those who come after us. Many of these buildings have been around for generations before us and it is our responsibility to hand them on in good condition to allow future generations to enjoy them too. So that the works you undertake do not damage the special qualities of a historic building, it is important to understand some of the basic principles of good building conservation. Many of these are common-sense and all are based on an understanding of how old buildings work and how, with sensitive treatment, they can stay special.

Before you start, learn as much as you can about your particular building. What is its history? How has it changed over time? Remember that later alterations may be important too and evidence that the building has been cared for and adapted over the years, with each generation adding its own layer to a unique history.

CARRYING OUT MAINTENANCE OR REPAIR WORKS

> Do use acknowledged experts - get independent and objective advice from the right people and only employ skilled craft workers with proven experience in the type of work required

> Do repair the parts of the building that need it - do not replace them unless they can no longer do the job they were designed to do

> Do make sure the right materials and repair techniques are used and that even the smallest changes you make to the building are done well

> Do use techniques that can be easily reversed or undone. This allows for any unforeseen problems to be corrected in future without damage to the special qualities of the building

> Do establish and understand the reasons for failure before undertaking repairs

> Do record all repair works for the benefit of future owners

> Don't overdo it – only do as much work to the building as is necessary, and as little as possible

> Don't look at problems in isolation – consider them in the context of the building as a whole

> Don't use architectural salvage from elsewhere unless you are certain that the taking of the materials hasn't caused the destruction of other old buildings or been the result of theft

1. A Short History of Ironwork in Ireland

The production of iron in Ireland

Iron has been produced and used for over 3,000 years, and used in Ireland for over 2,000 years. The early use of iron was limited by the technology available at the time. Early smelting practice used charcoal to fuel the furnaces, a labour-intensive process requiring vast amounts of fuel. As a result, iron was an expensive commodity and its use was generally limited to nails, hinges and grilles, swords, and other small-scale products.

The industry of smelting iron ore in Ireland experienced a dramatic rise and decline over the course of the seventeenth and eighteenth centuries, finally coming to an end in the mid nineteenth century.

Because Ireland had an abundance of timber, charcoal was far cheaper to purchase in Ireland than in Britain. This encouraged the development of a widespread and prosperous charcoal-fuelled iron industry. It is thought to have peaked around the year 1696-7,[1] when the export of iron from Ireland reached 1,692 tons.

As the industry developed across the country, vast expanses of Irish woodland were felled for the production of charcoal. The destructive nature of this exploitation meant that the iron industry shifted as local timber resources were exhausted. Although the English ironmasters running the operations in Ireland would have been well aware of the practice of coppicing, there appears to have been little or no attempt to implement this practice with Irish woodland.

The eighteenth century saw a steady decline in the iron industry in Ireland. This was due to the widespread depletion of Irish forests, combined with a later shift from the use of timber-based fuel (charcoal) to coal-based fuel (coke) to fire the furnaces. By the year 1740, Ireland was exporting only 14 tons of iron, but was importing 4,191 tons.[2] Competition from Britain, Sweden and other European countries with superior transport networks and native coal and iron ore reserves, further hastened this decline. In 1858, the last commercial iron smelting furnace in Ireland, at Creevalea, County Leitrim closed and no further attempts were made to smelt ore. In the second half of the nineteenth century, all the iron used in Ireland was imported, either as pig iron for conversion in Irish foundries, wrought iron, or as finished iron products.

Although Ireland possessed deposits of iron ore, these were often of poorer quality than those in Britain, making it necessary to combine native ores with higher quality imported British ores in order to produce satisfactory iron. Limited and ultimately unsuccessful attempts were made to smelt Irish ore using coal and peat. Ore was instead shipped to Britain where it was used as a flux, which helps slag to coalesce and float to the top of molten iron. In the 1870s and 1880s, Antrim was Ireland's biggest iron ore producer. For example, the production of iron ore at Glenravel Valley in Antrim peaked at 228,000 tons in 1880.[3]

Although the Irish iron-smelting industry would eventually cease in the nineteenth century, the use of iron in Ireland continued to increase. Iron, both structural and decorative, became a hugely popular material. Correspondingly, the number of foundries and ironworks in Dublin rose steadily through the course of the 1800s.

An article published in the *Irish Builder* (16th July 1863) reflects the popularity of the material at that time:

…We read of clear spans of 600 feet and upwards, skew bridges at angles of unheard-of obliquity, carriageways over and under railways, whole bazaars suspended in mid air. That iron should have superseded masonry and timber is not a matter of wonder if we consider the unparalleled advantages which it offers, not only from its affording strength combined with lightness, and from the facility with which it may be adapted to almost every purpose, but more especially with regard to economy of both time and money…. Nor is that most useful of metals limited in its adaptation to the construction of bridges alone, it is fast becoming a universal substance in almost every branch of manufacture…

---

1 Andrews, JH, Notes on the Historical Geography of the Irish Iron Industry, *Irish Geography*, Vol. 3, No. 3, 1956, p. 143

2 Andrews, JH, Op Cit

3 Hammond, Fred, *Antrim Coast & Glens: Industrial Heritage,* Department of the Environment for Northern Ireland, 1991, p.15

In 1780, John Dawson of Usher Street, Dublin, was the only iron founder specifically mentioned in street directories for that year. In the same year, only three smiths were listed. The building of the Irish railway network and the building boom of the mid nineteenth century created a high demand for iron. By 1860, the number of iron founders operating in Dublin had increased to 42. The number of smiths and ironworks had risen by this time to 23. It is likely that a similar trend occurred in other towns and cities across the country.

Turner glasshouse, Botanic Gardens, Dublin

Richard Turner

Perhaps one of the best known ironworkers in Ireland was Richard Turner (c.1798-1881) who was certainly no stranger to advertising in the Dublin Builder. *His grandfather, Timothy Turner, had produced ironwork for Trinity College Dublin, as Richard would also later go on to do. A section of railings supplied by him still encloses Trinity College, along College Street. Richard Turner is perhaps most famous, however, for his glasshouse at the Botanic Gardens in Dublin, and for his involvement in the design and production of the glasshouses at Belfast Botanic Gardens and the Royal Botanic Gardens at Kew, outside London. His son, William, later went on to take over the business – the Hammersmith Ironworks at Ballsbridge in Dublin – and also took on the Oxmantown Foundry and Ironworks on North King Street*

During the nineteenth century most towns and cities across Ireland had local foundries and blacksmiths, many of which advertised in the *Irish Builder* and the *Dublin Builder*. Foundries and ironworks were fuelled by imported coal and coke and used foreign iron as their raw material. Consequently they were usually located close to ports. Records kept by Thomas Sheridan, a successful smith and bell founder working in Dublin in the latter half of the nineteenth century, make regular references to orders of iron and coal being shipped in from Scotland and England around the year 1842. [4]

Numerous foundries focused on millwrighting, engineering, or heavy castings but also produced smaller-scale decorative ironwork. There were a number of large operations in Dublin: Tonge & Taggart supplied many Dublin coalhole covers, while Hammond Lane produced the lamp standards that line the streets of Rathmines. Cork had several large foundries, such as Perrott and Hive Ironworks. Musgrave & Co. of Belfast was a significant operation known for its patented stable and agricultural fittings, which were exported around the world, and also for larger structures such as the bandstands in St Stephen's Green and Phoenix Park, Dublin. Makers are often identifiable, thanks to their name cast into ironwork, or stamped onto wrought ironwork.

Musgrave & Co.'s name cast into the column of a bandstand in Phoenix Park, Dublin

---

4 James Sheridan papers, Business Records Survey DUB 114, National Archives, Dublin

Gates made by J & C McGloughlin Ltd are often easily recognisable by their distinctive gate latch

Blacksmiths often stamped their name on the flat slam bar (or cover plate) of gates

The Perrott Hive Foundry in Cork was one of the largest in the city in the late nineteenth century

The number of iron foundries listed in post office directories began to decline after 1860. The construction of the railways and the great building boom were winding down. Enormous companies, such as the Scottish firm Walter Macfarlane & Co., were thriving at this time and exporting their products throughout the world. It is likely that the competition from such companies, which were highly adept at marketing, helped to put many Irish foundries out of business. Also, although cast iron was still used extensively for architectural castings, iron was being steadily replaced in popularity by steel. Henry Bessemer had patented a method of mass-producing steel in 1856 and mild steel, which was stronger than wrought iron, had almost completely replaced the use of wrought iron in building construction by the end of the nineteenth century.

The fashion and demand for decorative ironwork continued to wane after the First World War, and dwindled almost completely after the Second World War. Foundries were forced to change their focus from decorative castings. Many turned to the production of fire escapes, building façades, windows, and other such products in order to stay afloat. The period between the wars also saw the growing use of modern welding techniques, which gradually superseded the more traditional blacksmithing. The remainder of the twentieth century witnessed a continuing decline in the production of architectural ironwork, which by this time had become unfashionable. The 1980s in particular were a very bad decade for foundries and saw the closure of numerous Dublin firms, many of which had been operating for a century or more.

The use of ironwork

From the eighteenth century onwards, as iron became more plentiful and affordable, it rapidly grew in popularity and came to be widely used in architectural decoration and embellishment. Its strength, versatility and durability made it the new building material of choice. These qualities would eventually change the face of architecture and engineering by enabling structures to be designed in previously impossible ways. As the concept of urban design became increasingly popular, newly developed streets and squares came to be bounded, enclosed, and demarcated by iron railings. In the eighteenth century, such railings were generally made entirely of wrought iron and were quite plain, complementing the Georgian architecture they adjoined. Very early wrought iron railings, dating to the first half of the eighteenth century, can be seen lining many of the houses along Henrietta Street, Dublin, and slightly later ones (1760s) on Parnell Square in Dublin and North Mall in Cork. These wrought iron railings were often complemented by decorative details such as cast urns, wrought iron lamp arches, or pillars decorated with fine scrollwork.

Early eighteenth-century wrought iron railings, Henrietta Street, Dublin. The large-scale development of squares and terraces from the 1700s onwards fuelled a rising demand for iron railings

In the late eighteenth and early nineteenth centuries, cast iron was increasingly incorporated into ornamental ironwork. For example, a gate frame made of wrought iron would be embellished by ornate cast iron infill panels, husks, finials, and collars. Railings with wrought iron bars topped by a diverse range of ornamental cast iron finials also became widespread. Wrought iron railings and gates embellished with cast iron details can be found in virtually every town and city across Ireland.

Early nineteenth-century railings incorporating fashionable Neo-Classical decoration such as cast iron collars, husks, and anthemion (honeysuckle) finials

Mid nineteenth-century railings with wrought iron bars and rails, and decorative cast iron finials and husks

By the 1890s and early 1900s, entire railing panels cast in iron were becoming increasingly widespread. Cork, Dublin, Dundalk and Limerick have some superb examples. While much of this cast ironwork was made by local foundries, a significant proportion was also imported from England and Scotland. The production of cast ironwork had developed into a booming industry there and manufacturers, many of whom had offices in Ireland as well, produced extensive catalogues displaying an enormous variety of designs for railings, gates, rainwater goods, doorcases, balconies, lamp standards and other architectural components.

The ability to mass-produce cast iron also led to the widespread installation of rainwater goods (gutters, downpipes and hoppers). Before the availability of cast iron, rainwater goods were often made of lead, an expensive material, and were generally confined to buildings of high status. The advent of mass-produced cast iron made them more affordable to the growing middle classes and saw their widespread incorporation into virtually all new buildings from the nineteenth century. The versatility of cast iron also meant that many designs were highly ornate.

Cast iron gutter brackets, typical of the second half of the nineteenth century

Eighteenth- and nineteenth-century boot scrapers are still a common feature of houses across Ireland

Iron was to have a profound impact on building design. The use of iron beams, which could span far greater distances than those made of timber, combined with the use of iron columns, enabled architects to design larger, airier, more open floor spaces as thick supporting walls were no longer required. The Victorian era nurtured a growing interest in communal structures. Across Ireland, bandstands and ornamental fountains were installed in parks and along sea fronts. Drinking fountains too became popular, largely due to the Temperance Movement. An impressive reproduction fountain and canopy, the original of which was made by Walter Macfarlane & Co. of Glasgow, was reinstated on the Dun Laoghaire seafront in 2003. Some wonderful examples of bandstands survive in Youghal, made by McDowall Steven & Co. of Glasgow; St Stephen's Green, Dublin, made by Musgraves of Belfast; and Blackrock, County Dublin, made by Tonge & Taggart of Dublin. Many ornamental fountains also survive around Ireland, for example the beautiful pair of spray fountains in the People's Park, Dun Laoghaire, made by George Smith & Co. of Glasgow. Ornate cast iron entrance canopies include those at the Olympia Theatre on Dame Street, Dublin, made by Walter Macfarlane & Co., and the fine canopy at the Mansion House on Dawson Street in Dublin, made by J & C McGloughlin of Dublin. The Arts and Crafts movement brought about a renewed interest in handcrafts, including wrought ironwork, and Edwardian terraces around Ireland abound with elegant wrought iron gates and railings. In fact, from the end of the nineteenth century, many cast iron designs tried to emulate the appearance of wrought iron.

Bandstand, Youghal, which was made by the Scottish firm McDowall Steven & Co.

Lurganboy Church of Ireland church, County Leitrim. A fine example of a corrugated-iron clad 'tin church' built in 1862

Corrugated iron

Corrugated iron was first patented in 1828 by Henry Robinson Palmer and was a popular material throughout the nineteenth century and into the opening decades of the twentieth. It was made by passing thin sheets of iron through rollers, which gave them extra strength and rigidity, and was available in a variety of lengths, sheet thicknesses, and profiles. Due to its lightness, cheapness, flexibility and ease of assembly, corrugated iron became a popular material. It was often used for roofing, sometimes covering earlier thatched roofs which were retained beneath. Corrugated iron was also used to make pre-fabricated structures, particularly vernacular, agricultural and religious buildings. These were usually formed using a timber frame clad with corrugated iron. Manufacturers developed a range of patented building designs, as well as fixings and features such as windows specifically designed for use with corrugated iron. It is important to retain as many of these original features as possible as replacements are no longer available.

There is a rich heritage of iron grave markers and grave surrounds to be found throughout the country. This example from Co. Offaly is marked with the maker's name – P & E Egan Tullamore

The National Concert Hall, Earlsfort Terrace, Dublin. Cast iron windows and spandrel panels became increasingly widespread from the start of the twentieth century. This example was supplied by the Scottish firm Walter Macfarlane & Co. Ltd in 1914

2. Maintenance of Historic Ironwork

Maintenance is one of the single most important factors in ensuring the long term durability of ironwork. Ironwork that has survived for over 100 years can give many more years of service, provided it is regularly maintained. Inspecting ironwork once a year will ensure that any developing problems or corrosion are caught early on, before they have had a chance to develop into more serious problems. Ironwork should be checked annually to make sure that the paint is in good condition, that there are no areas of developing corrosion, distortion, or fracturing, and that the supporting wall or ground is stable. Ironwork should be cleaned and painted at least once every five years.

Cleaning ironwork

Routine maintenance should include cleaning ironwork with water and a cloth, or a bristle brush if the soiling is light, so that dirt does not accumulate on the surface and trap moisture. Excessive amounts of water should not be used. High-pressure power hoses should not be used on historic ironwork as they can drive water into small cracks and crevices from where it will be difficult to dry out. Ironwork should be thoroughly dried off after cleaning. Localised areas of corrosion can be removed using a chisel, wire brush (preferably bronze wire) and sandpaper before painting over the cleaned metal. If routine maintenance is carried out, this should prevent more serious problems from developing, which would require far more time consuming and costly repairs at a later date.

Routine maintenance to ironwork, such as this attractive cast iron stall riser to a shopfront should include gentle washing using a minimum amount of water to remove accumulated dirt

The purpose of cleaning ironwork is to remove dirt, corrosion and, in some cases, existing layers of paint. Good surface preparation is necessary to ensure that new paint layers adhere properly to the iron surface and perform well. The degree of cleaning needed will depend on a number of factors, including the type and condition of ironwork (wrought or cast, robust or fragile) and the significance of any underlying paint, coatings, or decorative schemes. These may contain valuable and irreplaceable information on historic paint schemes, such as the decorative history of the element and the paint technology used. Other factors, such as the presence of mill scale (a stable oxide layer on the surface of iron which has a protective function) may also influence the choice of cleaning method.

In some cases, the existing paint may be reasonably sound and it will only be necessary to remove surface dirt with water, and small localised areas of corrosion using a chisel, wire brush and sandpaper before repainting. Where corrosion or paint decay are more severe, it may be necessary to clean ironwork back to bare metal to provide the best base surface for fresh paint. The current recommended international standard for cleaning is the Swedish Standard, with SA $2\frac{1}{2}$ (very thorough blast cleaning) the most commonly applied.

Certain levels of cleaning may not be appropriate for different types and condition of traditional ironwork. The method used to clean ironwork should always be considered carefully. Some methods are more appropriate than others, and using the wrong cleaning technique can damage ironwork. Cleaning back to bare metal can be problematic. It removes all traces of previous coatings, destroying any evidence of earlier decorative schemes. To overcome this, it might be feasible to retain either a strip or patches of the existing paint layers that are of particular merit (preferably in areas that get the least direct sunlight), cleaning all other areas of the ironwork back to bare metal.

Cleaning to SA $2\frac{1}{2}$ is also problematic for wrought iron. When wrought iron was made, the rolling process produced a surface layer referred to as 'mill scale' which is widely considered to protect ironwork from corrosion. Cleaning wrought ironwork to SA $2\frac{1}{2}$ standard will remove this mill scale and the protection it provides the iron. Tooling marks can also be lost by overly-aggressive cleaning techniques. However, there are a number of cleaning techniques, outlined below, that can be sensitive enough to allow a skilled operator to retain the mill scale layer.

Swedish Standard for cleaning steel:

SA 1: Light blast cleaning

SA 2: Thorough blast cleaning

SA 2½: Very thorough blast cleaning

SA 3: Blast cleaning to visually clean steel

Methods of cleaning ironwork

CLEANING WITH WATER

Cleaning ironwork by hand with water, or water mixed with detergent, will remove light dirt and grease. Low pressure water can also be an effective means of cleaning light, superficial dirt from painted ironwork. High-pressure washing will not be appropriate. Fragile ironwork will be damaged by the pressure, and water can be driven into cracks and fissures where, unless allowed to dry out thoroughly, it will lodge and potentially cause damage to paint coatings.

MANUAL CLEANING

Cleaning by hand using a chisel, wire brush and sandpaper is the most economical method of cleaning ironwork. However, care should be taken not to damage or score the surface of fragile ironwork. This method is not as effective as other cleaning methods at removing all rust and dirt, and is most appropriate for mild, localised areas of corrosion.

MECHANICAL TOOLS

Hand-held tools such as grinders and rotary brushes are more efficient than manual cleaning, but still will not remove corrosion and dirt from narrow joints and difficult-to-reach areas. Such tools must be used with extreme caution, and only by an experienced craftsperson as, in the wrong hands, they can cause damage to the surface of ironwork and are likely to remove the mill scale surface from wrought iron. Needle guns offer an effective means of removing heavy corrosion by means of needle heads which pound the iron surface, but are also unable to clean hard-to-reach areas such as joints.

A needle gun can be effective at removing corrosion material, but can be damaging to the surface of ironwork if applied with too much pressure (Image courtesy of Historic Scotland)

FLAME CLEANING

This is a traditional and common means of cleaning wrought iron in particular. A flame is passed over the surface of the iron (or it is placed on the forge) to soften paint and loosen corrosion material, which can then be brushed off. Flame cleaning should only be carried out by an experienced craftsperson. The use of a blow torch poses a significant fire hazard, and care should be taken to implement all necessary precautions and safe working practices. Some building owners and institutions may have a ban on the use of such 'hot working' practices.

CHEMICAL CLEANING

Chemical cleaners can offer an effective means of removing thick layers of paint while retaining delicate surface features such as mill scale and tooling. However, they should be used with caution and only by an experienced craftsperson. Ironwork should be thoroughly cleaned and rinsed with water to remove all traces of chemicals. The chemical may soak beneath the surface of the ironwork, despite thorough rinsing, making it difficult to remove completely. This can have long-term effects. If some of the chemical remains in the iron it can damage the paintwork and may corrode the iron internally.

ACID DIPPING OR ACID PICKLING

This method is used to remove corrosion material from ironwork and involves submerging ironwork in a vat of dilute phosphoric or sulphuric acid. This type of cleaning should only be carried out by an experienced craftsperson. It is an effective means of removing corrosion without damaging the surface of the ironwork. However, as with chemical cleaners, there is the risk that acid may soak into crevices and cracks and lead to future corrosion of the metal. It is therefore essential to thoroughly rinse the iron immediately after acid dipping to remove as much of the chemical as possible. The use of hydrochloric acid or sodium hydroxide (caustic soda) is not recommended.

BLAST CLEANING

Blast cleaning is a standard means of cleaning cast iron and is also used for wrought iron. Due to the health hazard posed by surviving layers of lead paint which might be disturbed and become airborne during the cleaning process, appropriate personal protection equipment should be worn and all other appropriate precautions taken when carrying out blast cleaning. The process involves blasting grit under pressure onto the surface of ironwork. The pressure can be adjusted. It is generally best to start at a low pressure and gradually increase it until the desired pressure is achieved. Fragile sections of iron, particularly delicate wrought ironwork such as leaf-work, can be vulnerable to damage if the pressure is too high. Blast cleaning should therefore be done with caution by an expert craftsperson and is best avoided for delicate or fine wrought ironwork.

A variety of blast mediums can be used, ranging from inert mineral grit to glass beads, plastic pellets, and crushed walnut shells. Sand used as a blast medium is now subject to an international ban due to the danger of silicosis. The use of chilled iron and copper slag is not recommended. An inert mineral grit is one of the most effective blast mediums for cast iron, and will provide a good surface for new paint. For more delicate or high-end conservation work, glass beads and crushed walnut shells provide a more sensitive blast medium. Plastic pellets can be particularly effective for cleaning wrought iron as they are less hard than other mediums and may enable the original mill scale layer to be retained. If work is to be carried out on ironwork in situ, it may be necessary to consult with the local authority to ensure that this cleaning method is permitted. Blast cleaning may not be possible on-site due to issues concerning waste disposal and other health and safety implications. Where blast cleaning is to be carried out on ironwork in situ it is important to ensure that surrounding materials are carefully protected and that appropriate safety measures are taken to protect members of the public.

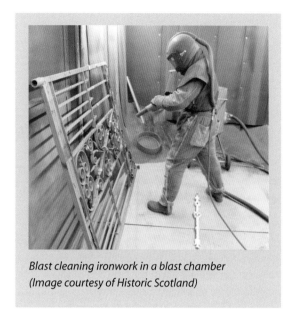

Blast cleaning ironwork in a blast chamber (Image courtesy of Historic Scotland)

WET BLAST CLEANING

Wet blast cleaning is an effective means of removing soluble salts that have been deposited on the surface of iron, particularly in marine environments, and is also a means of reducing dust levels when removing lead-based paints. However, there is the risk that water may be driven deep into cracks in the ironwork. This could initiate corrosion, and might damage fresh coats of paint if they were applied to iron which retained some moisture. This method of cleaning requires an expert craftsperson. Special care should be taken to ensure that run-off is disposed of in accordance with environmental regulations.

Painting ironwork

Paint is generally applied to ironwork for two reasons: to protect the iron against corrosion, and for decorative purposes. Other coatings have also been used to protect iron in the past, such as linseed oil (more common for use on indoor ironwork) and galvanizing (applying a coating of zinc). Historically, lead-based paints were the most generally used and were a highly effective form of protection. However, the presence of lead paint can make cleaning ironwork and removing old layers of paint problematic due to the toxicity of lead and lead paint should only be removed in compliance with the relevant safety standards. The gradual build-up of many layers of paint over the years provides increased protection to ironwork, although it has the disadvantage of obscuring decorative detail.

TAKING PAINT SAMPLES

Original layers of paint often survive beneath modern coatings. If historically significant ironwork is to be cleaned and re-painted, it may be worth taking samples of the existing paint layers for analysis. Analysis should be able to determine the colour and type of paint used for earlier coatings. It is advisable to take samples from more than one part of the ironwork. Historically, colour schemes were often polychromatic and certain details may have been picked out in different colours or gilding.

A reasonably strong blade is needed for taking paint samples (plus a number of replacement blades on stand-by in case the blade breaks), as old layers of lead paint can be difficult to cut through. The proper analysis of paint samples is a scientific process and not to be confused with the practice known as 'paint scraping' where paint is simply scraped off until the earliest coating is revealed. Caution is advised in this regard, as different colours were often used for the primer, base coat, and top coat, which may cause confusion when trying to determine the colour of earlier decorative schemes. See also page 37.

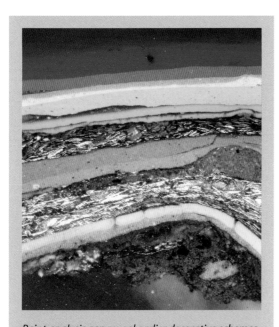

Paint analysis can reveal earlier decorative schemes which have been hidden under more recent layers of paint. Analysis of this paint fragment revealed a number of earlier layers of gilding
(Image courtesy of Historic Scotland)

SURFACE PREPARATION

Whether the existing paint is to be used as a base, or a new paint system is to be applied to bare metal, good surface preparation is essential to ensure a long-lasting, durable coating. Paint is the first line of defence for ironwork, and if the surface has not been properly prepared, the paint will not adhere or perform well. All rust, dirt, grease and chemical deposits such as soluble salts should be thoroughly cleaned from the surface before painting. It is especially important to clean off all rust, particularly at vulnerable points such as the meeting surfaces of collars, finials, fixings and other constructional detailing and rails on railings and gates. If rust is not removed, it is likely to continue to develop underneath the paint.

Different paint systems require different levels of surface preparation and these should be checked with the paint manufacturer. The degree to which iron is to be cleaned prior to painting can be classified according to the Swedish Standard as outlined above. However, it should be borne in mind that certain levels of cleaning may not be appropriate for different types and conditions of traditional ironwork (for example, in the case of a project where it is deemed important to retain the original oxide or mill scale layer).

If ironwork is to be professionally cleaned back to bare metal it is essential that the ironwork is stored in dry conditions. This will prevent moisture from being trapped beneath fresh coats of paint, which might cause damage to the paint coatings at a later time when the ambient temperature rises.

PAINTING ON TOP OF EXISTING COATINGS

It may be possible to retain existing paint and either touch it up in patches, or use it as a base for fresh paint. The choice made will depend on the condition of the ironwork, whether there is corrosion occurring, and the condition of the paint. If the existing paint is to be retained, its compatibility with new paint will need to be determined. The paint manufacturer can be consulted on this. It is also possible to carry out a simple patch test; paint a small section and allow it to dry for 48 hours. Any problems of incompatibility are likely to show up within this period.

The surface should be thoroughly cleaned before fresh paint is applied. Any areas of corrosion should be removed completely by chipping rust away and using a wire brush and sandpaper to clean the surface thoroughly to prevent it spoiling the new coat of paint. Areas of sound paint can be cleaned by washing with water, or by wiping down with white spirits and allowing them to dry thoroughly. Next, existing paint should be sanded lightly to form a good key for the next layer of paint. Any areas of damaged paint that need to be patched should be sanded back to a smooth edge before new paint is applied. New paint should overlap the existing by about 50mm.

CHOOSING THE RIGHT PAINT SYSTEM

When it comes to re-painting traditional ironwork, there are generally two options: either a traditional paint system or a modern one can be used. If historic and aesthetic authenticity is important, traditional paint may be the preferred choice. A new coating should aim to match the original (if this can be identified) not only in colour but also in surface texture, composition, and sheen level. Even if the composition of the original historic paint cannot be matched, for example if permission cannot be obtained to use lead-based paint, it should still be possible to match the texture and colour of the original scheme. Modern paint production allows colours to be matched very closely to those derived from paint samples.

Traditional paints have proven their effectiveness and durability over centuries of wear. Red lead paint was one of the most common forms of primer for iron, and was usually painted over with oil-based (usually linseed) paints containing lead. Bitumen and pitch were used over a primer to coat corrugated iron. Corrugated iron was commonly galvanized from the end of the nineteenth century. Nowadays the use of lead-based paints is controlled due to their toxicity. Their use can be licensed by the Health & Safety Authority for use on certain types of historic buildings. However, red lead paint is still widely available (particularly from chandlers). There are no restrictions on its use as a paint because it is less toxic than paint containing white lead.

Traditional paints can be highly effective. However, when deciding to use such paints, it is important to consider future painting; how likely are future owners or caretakers of the ironwork to use traditional paints? Will the paint system be compatible with modern

paints if these are applied in the future? The best approach to be taken should be decided on a case-by-case basis, as factors such as the historical significance of the ironwork, budget available, and required performance will vary from project to project. For some projects, a modern paint system may be more suitable. There are many types of modern coating systems on the market, many of which are highly effective. Paint manufacturers will normally guarantee their systems for a set number of years although such guarantees do not negate the need for regular inspections and maintenance, and ironwork should always be inspected long before the given number of years to first maintenance.

BEST PRACTICE FOR PAINTING BARE METAL

Current best practice recommends the following system:

> Two coats of a zinc-based primer

> One or two base coats of micaceous iron oxide (MIO)

> One or two top coats of gloss paint

A dry film thickness (DFT) of no more than about 250 microns is generally recommended. This is the thickness to which the layers of paint dry. DFT measures can be bought from many hardware stores. Hard-shell epoxy paints are not recommended as these are not flexible enough to allow for the natural thermal expansion and contraction of iron.

CHOOSING A COLOUR SCHEME

Where a historic colour scheme can be identified through the analysis of paint samples, it may be desirable to reinstate the earlier or original paint scheme. However, changes in colour may require planning permission so it is advisable to consult the relevant local authority before undertaking repainting.

Gilding was sometimes applied to highlight certain features of the ironwork. Gold paint is a frequent substitute for gold leaf but tends to weather to a dull and unattractive brown. Gilding is not overly expensive or complicated to do, and provides far better long-term results. However, gilding may not be appropriate in some circumstances – for instance, railings around a terraced property where neighbouring properties do not have gilded ironwork.

APPLYING PAINT

If paint is not properly applied to ironwork, or if the surface has not been correctly prepared to receive the paint, the new coating will be less effective and may even fail. Ironwork can usually be cleaned and painted more effectively in workshop conditions. However, budget and time constraints may prohibit this, and it may be unnecessary if there is little corrosion or damage to the existing paint. The decision to remove ironwork should also be balanced against the potential damage that its removal could cause to adjoining masonry or to the ironwork itself. This is particularly relevant with regard to wrought iron, as it is usually necessary to break many of the joints in order to dismantle wrought ironwork.

Whether ironwork is painted indoors or outdoors, it is important that it is absolutely dry before paint is applied. If there is any moisture within the iron (due to rainfall, dew, or even high relative humidity) this will be trapped beneath fresh layers of paint and is likely to cause corrosion within a short period of time. In general, ironwork should not be painted outdoors between December and February, as damp conditions and low temperatures can hinder the curing of paint. Painting in windy conditions must also be avoided as wind-blown dirt and dust may damage fresh coatings of paint.

For larger projects, it is essential to get the paint right. The specification of paint should be chosen carefully, and, whatever system is chosen, it should be applied in a controlled environment. This will ensure that the iron is completely dry before the paint is applied, and will also prevent any wind-blown dust and dirt from damaging the paint while it is drying. Generally, hand-application of paint by brush is better than spraying as it is more effective at reaching sections that are out of the line of sight. For paint to be effective, an adequate number of coats must be applied. When painting bare metal, use at least two coats of primer, followed by at least one base coat and a top coat. Several layers of primer can be far more effective than an expensive top coat.

Coats must be applied in thin layers, allowing each to dry thoroughly before the next coat is applied. This prevents solvents evaporating from the layer underneath and damaging subsequent coats painted on top. If paint is applied too thickly it obscures detail, is unlikely to cure properly, and will be less effective as a result. Paint that is improperly applied to uneven surfaces may bridge depressions and hollows instead

Over-thick application of paint will obscure detail and result in less effective protection

of adhering to them. This causes air to be trapped between the paint and the metal, making the paint more prone to cracking and flaking. When dealing with traditional galvanised corrugated iron, a mordant wash or chemical etching primer is required to help the paint to adhere to the galvanised surface.

If ironwork has been painted off-site, a final inspection should be conducted once the ironwork has been reinstated. This will ensure that any localised areas of damage that may have occurred during transit and assembly are identified immediately and can be repainted in situ to prevent these becoming weak points in the new coating.

This photograph shows a set of railings a month after they were painted. Corrosion material was not thoroughly removed before the application of paint resulting in the localised failure of the new paint

FILLERS AND SEALANTS

Paint cannot bridge gaps, so fillers and sealants are an integral part of any coating system. They waterproof joints and seams, and can re-profile water traps and casting defects so that they shed water properly. Traditionally, red lead paste (still available from chandlers) was used to caulk large joints. Putty and white lead paste were often used for smaller joints. White lead is not likely to be an acceptable material to use today because of its toxicity. Modern polysulphide mastics can be used as an effective alternative to traditional fillers.

A new section of gate, based on the design of the adjacent gate at the entrance to Leinster House, Dublin. To prevent corrosion, water traps should be filled so that they shed water, or pinholes drilled at the base to allow water to escape (although drilling into original fabric should be avoided where possible)

Paint cannot fill holes. Casting flaws such as those pictured above should be filled to prevent water becoming trapped and causing corrosion to develop

Getting the right advice

In the case of the architectural ironwork on your property, you will usually be able to carry out basic maintenance inspections and repair works yourself. But when it comes to commissioning repair works, it is important to know when specialist advice is needed and where to find the right help. The repair of ironwork requires particular craftsmanship and expertise, and further advice is given elsewhere in this booklet. It is a false economy not to get the best advice before having work carried out. Bad repair works can damage ironwork in the long-term, devalue your property as a whole, and be difficult and expensive to undo.

You will need the right advice for the particular job. Sometimes you will require a craftsman such as a blacksmith. Works to larger or more complex ironwork structures will require the services of a suitably qualified architect, a surveyor, or a structural engineer. Sometimes, a multi-disciplinary team may be required. Most importantly, you should ensure that any adviser is independent and objective, not someone trying to sell you something or with a vested interest in increasing the scale and expense of work. You need someone who understands historic ironwork, has experience in dealing with it, and has trained to work with it. He or she should be knowledgeable and experienced in dealing with your type of building and the ironwork associated with it. Many building professionals and contractors are principally involved with modern construction and may not know how to deal sympathetically with an old building. Do not choose a person or company based on cost alone. The cheapest quote you receive may be from a person who does not fully understand the complexity of the problem.

When employing a professional adviser, or a building contractor, or an ironwork specialist, check their qualifications and status with the relevant bodies and institutes first. Ask for references and for the locations and photographs of recent similar work undertaken. Do not be afraid to follow up the references and to visit other projects. A good practitioner won't mind you doing this and, in the case of ironwork repair, it will usually be important to see the completed work at first hand rather than to rely simply on photographs. If you see a good job successfully completed, find out who did the work, whether they would be suitable for the works you want to undertake and if the building owner was satisfied.

Be clear when briefing your adviser what you want him or her to do. A good adviser should be able to undertake an inspection of your property, give you a report identifying the causes of damage, make a careful diagnosis of the problem, recommend repairs, specify the work required, get a firm price from a suitable builder or craftsman, and oversee the work in situ as it progresses. If your building and its architectural ironwork is likely to need ongoing works over a number of years, your relationship with your adviser, builder, or ironworker will be important both to you and your building, and continuity will be a great advantage. They will be able to become familiar with the property and to understand how it acts, and will build up expertise based on your particular building.

The Royal Institute of the Architects of Ireland keeps a register of architects accredited in building conservation and will be able to provide you with a list. The Irish Georgian Society maintains a register of practitioners with traditional building and conservation skills, including ironworkers. The Construction Industry Federation has a register of heritage contractors. The conservation officer in your local authority may be able to recommend suitable professionals, craft workers, or suppliers in your area. The Irish Artist Blacksmiths Association can offer advice on local blacksmiths.

3. The Deterioration and Decay of Ironwork

The deterioration of ironwork is caused by three factors:

> Chemical corrosion (rusting)

> Galvanic corrosion (also known as electrochemical or bi-metallic corrosion)

> Mechanical action

Additionally, more general factors that set up the conditions necessary for deterioration and damage include:

> Inherent faults in the original manufacture

> Lack of maintenance

> Moisture

> Poor workmanship

> The use of substitute materials

> Inappropriate alterations

> Disuse, neglect and vandalism

CHECKING FOR CORROSION

When checking for corrosion pay particular attention to the following areas:

> Water traps are vulnerable spots for corrosion to occur. They are often caused by design flaws, particularly where hollow or cupped details are not filled, profiled, or pierced to shed water. Water traps can also be created by flaking paint or expanding rust

> Water can seep into joints and so care should be taken to ensure that all joints are properly caulked (filled), either with traditional red lead paste or a polysulphide mastic. Traditionally, bolts and screw heads were caulked to protect them and to hide them from view

> Masonry sockets can be vulnerable if lead holding the ironwork in place begins to break down. The gudgeon (also known as the heel cup) of a gate is the hole that receives the foot of the gate which swivels as it opens and closes. This can be prone to corrosion as water tends to lodge there

> Horizontal elements of ironwork tend to suffer more corrosion than other parts. This is because water often lies on the flat surface, or may drip continuously from above. Corrosion may even occur on the underside of rails where drops of water hang for long periods of time before falling away

> Vegetation can trap and transfer moisture, and has the added disadvantage of hiding corrosion from view. Acids and chemicals in plants can also be harmful to ironwork and their growing roots and tendrils can damage structures

An oxide layer has developed on this wrought iron handrail which protects it from further corrosion

Broken, flaking paint traps and holds water to the iron, preventing it from drying out properly, and can lead to corrosion. Areas of chipped paint are not as significant a threat so long as the iron is in an exposed location and is able to dry out. Nevertheless, such chips should be treated as soon as possible to prevent rust from forming

Water traps, such as the void areas behind these leaf details, will cause corrosion to develop at a faster rate

Corrosion (chemical and galvanic)

Iron is in its most stable state when it exists as part of iron ore. This is its state of equilibrium with the surrounding environment. Any form of processing – smelting the iron ore to extract the iron, re-melting, hammering, etc – will change the chemical make-up of iron so that it is no longer in a stable state. From this moment on, the iron will constantly attempt to return to its state of equilibrium, in other words, to how it was when it was ore. This is essentially what is happening when iron corrodes. The process of corrosion is really the iron's way of returning to its stable state, to the condition it was in before it was dug out of the ground. Ironwork which is situated indoors usually remains stable due to the lack of moisture to activate corrosion. However, corrosion can be severe in coastal areas due to the presence of salts in the atmosphere. These salts are deposited on the surface of the iron where they dissolve and increase the speed of electron exchange between the iron and oxygen, creating corrosion material at a faster rate.

CHEMICAL CORROSION (RUSTING)

Chemical corrosion occurs when iron oxidises (part of the iron molecules – the electrons – combine with oxygen in the air). The metal literally 'loses' parts of itself when it corrodes. This process produces the corrosion product – rust. For corrosion to occur there must usually be both water and air present. Air contains the oxygen with which the electrons from the iron combine. The water acts as an electrolyte – this is a solution containing salts which enables the release of electrons from the iron. Any form of moisture can act as an electrolyte – dew, condensation, or moisture in soil.

GALVANIC CORROSION

Galvanic corrosion occurs when two dissimilar metals are placed in direct contact with one another in the presence of an electrolyte (e.g. rainwater). One metal will corrode sacrificially to the other – for example, aluminium will corrode at an accelerated rate when put in contact with wrought iron. Different metals will lose or gain electrons more or less readily and this is known as their 'electrode potential.' Each metal's electrode potential is shown on what is known as the Electrochemical Series, which places metals higher or lower on the list depending on how easily they will lose their electrons. A metal which is lower down on the list will give up its electrons more easily than a metal that is higher on the list – so for instance, zinc, which is lower down on the list than iron, will give up its electrons more easily than iron. If zinc and iron are placed in contact with one another and left exposed to air and rain, zinc will corrode sacrificially to the iron.

The process of galvanic corrosion is used as an advantage with products such as paint containing zinc. When the paint surface becomes scratched or chipped, the zinc corrodes sacrificially to the iron thereby diverting corrosion from the iron. An added benefit is that the corrosion products of zinc are relatively stable so that they form a protective barrier over the surface of the iron.

Galvanic corrosion is occurring between the original wrought iron gate frame and the metal of the filler rod that was used to form the weld joint attaching the gate catch to the gate frame

Wrought iron typically 'delaminates' as it corrodes, accentuating the fibrous structure of the material

The development of corrosion

As the volume of rust is up to eight times greater than that of iron, even though a section of iron may appear at first glance to be completely corroded, it is possible that there is a significant amount of sound iron beneath the corrosion. However, developing corrosion material can exert great pressure on surrounding ironwork causing significant damage such as cracking, fractures, damage to surrounding masonry, and eventual failure of the structure. As wrought iron corrodes it will often delaminate (the rust appears to develop in layers and takes on a fibrous appearance similar to wood). Cast iron corrosion tends to flake and crumble rather than develop in expanding layers. The force of expanding corrosion may cause wrought iron to bend and distort before it eventually breaks. However, cast iron is unable to accommodate the same degree of movement and is therefore more likely to fracture and fail without warning where expanding corrosion exerts pressure.

Where rust forms a continuous, unbroken and often glossy layer on the surface of ironwork, it can in fact act as a protective barrier. This is commonly seen on wrought iron handrails that have a smooth sheen on their surface. But where rust develops and expands in flaking, laminated layers it causes real damage. It acts as a moisture trap, which in turn accelerates the formation of more rust.

Mechanical action

The most common types of mechanical deterioration are caused by unstable or settling foundations and impact damage. Unstable foundations, corrosion of the base in which iron elements are anchored, or the settling of ground beneath ironwork can all cause instability, fracturing and deterioration of the ironwork.

Impact damage caused for example by vandalism or cars, can cause deformation (in the case of wrought iron) and fracturing or shattering (in the case of cast iron)

4. Repairing Ironwork

This chapter outlines a selection of repair and conservation approaches that can be taken to address some of the most commonly encountered problems that arise with ironwork. Specific repair techniques are dealt with in more detail in chapter 6.

Decorative ironwork

1. Railings

2. Gates

3. Balconies, balconettes, and window guards

4. Rainwater goods

5. Finials and weathervanes

1. Railings

Railings are among the most commonly encountered items of decorative ironwork. This section looks at some of the most common problems that arise and suggests how these problems might be rectified.

FRACTURED OR MISSING CAST IRON FINIALS, HUSKS, AND COLLARS

Irish railings commonly consist of wrought iron bars with cast iron husks, collars, and finials, held together by an upper and lower rail, supported on feet. A frequent problem with cast iron finials, husks and collars is that their shape traps water, causes corrosion to develop, and they are eventually lost due to fracturing. Foundries that specialise in traditional casting usually have a large stock of patterns, and it is quite often possible to find a match for missing cast iron embellishments. Alternatively, a pattern-maker can make a new pattern. Existing finials should never be cut off to provide a template for new castings. Where matching patterns do not exist, it may be better to leave the railings as they are rather than damage them further.

New castings should be put in place in the traditional way. Finials should never be welded in place. Finials can be slotted over the original spiked end of the wrought iron bar (if it exists) and hammered or

secured in place by hot-poured lead. There is often a hole in the finial which allows lead to be poured into the hollow of the finial. If the spike does not survive, the finial can be pinned in place. Welding new castings in place is not recommended.

The hollow interior of the finial should be well painted before being put in place to prevent the cast iron from coming into direct contact with the wrought iron. The advantage of fixing finials in place with hot-poured lead is that it prevents the cast iron finial coming into direct contact with the wrought iron spike.

Missing cast iron finials, collars, and husks are common due to the development of galvanic corrosion between these decorative elements and the wrought iron bar that they are usually placed over. It is generally possible to cast and fit new finials, although husks and collars below the top rail can be more problematic to replace due to the need to dismantle the railings in order to place them in position

DISTORTION OF WROUGHT IRON CAUSED BY DEVELOPING CORROSION

Where the build-up of corrosion material (rust) is distorting ironwork, it may be necessary to dismantle the ironwork so that the corroding sections can be thoroughly cleaned, reshaped and painted to prevent further damage. The slam bars (also known as cover plates) of gates are particularly vulnerable to this type of damage.

CORROSION OF THE RAILS

Top and bottom rails may suffer localised corrosion around the bases of finials and collars. The rail allows water to lie on its flat surface, which encourages galvanic corrosion between the cast iron finial and wrought iron rail. This type of corrosion results in loss of material and 'pitting' around the base of the finial. Minor pitting will not compromise the structural stability of a rail, although the pitting may cause continuing and accelerated corrosion by trapping more water. The corrosion material should be thoroughly cleaned off, taking care to clean the joint between the finial and the rail as well as possible. The rail should then be re-profiled using an epoxy resin so that it sheds water more efficiently.

If the corrosion is severe, it may be necessary to remove the corroded areas and piece-in new wrought iron. Mild steel should preferably not be used, as this can create further potential for galvanic corrosion by introducing a third type of metal to the railing. Problems will be further compounded if modern welding techniques are used. Ideally, wrought iron should be forge-welded in place but, where this is not possible, a stainless steel piece should be carefully welded into position, taking care to remove all weld splatter. The new metal should be well painted and regularly maintained to ensure that it remains isolated from the surrounding cast and wrought iron in the future.

Where new rails are installed, traditional detailing should be matched where possible, such as piercing bars through the rail

SECTIONS OF THE RAIL ARE COMING APART

This can either be caused by advanced corrosion as described above, or by corrosion of the fixings (usually wrought iron pins) holding individual sections of rail together. The joint – normally a 'scarf' joint where the ends of each section overlap each other and are held together by the pin – can be re-secured using a stainless steel pin which should be isolated from surrounding material using a nylon sleeve or washer. Care should be taken to match new fittings to the originals, which traditionally were straight bars hammered into rounded caps, top and bottom, to secure them in place.

Corrosion developing at a scarf joint

MISSING FIXINGS (SCREWS, BOLTS, PINS, ETC)

Original fixings were usually made of wrought iron, and have often corroded away. Mild steel or galvanised mild steel fixings do not have good corrosion resistance and are not recommended as replacements. Stainless steel or phosphor bronze fixings are preferable, and should be isolated from the surrounding ironwork by means of nylon sleeves or 'top hats' which are readily available and inexpensive.

The design and shape of fixings has changed over time. The size of screw threads, for example, did not become standardised until the mid-nineteenth century. Square-headed bolts were common in the 1800s, and hex-head bolts did not emerge until the early decades of the twentieth century. When replacing missing fixings do not ignore the shape and style of the originals. Fixings are an important part of the overall character and aesthetic of historic ironwork.

BROKEN BACKSTAYS

Backstays occasionally become loose or detached from railings. Where the backstays are of wrought iron, this problem is usually caused by the corrosion and failure of the pin that holds them in place. If the backstays are made of cast iron, settlement of the wall supporting the railings may cause the railings to shift, exerting pressure on the cast iron backstays, eventually causing them to fracture. Wrought iron backstays should not be reattached by welding. Other stays found on the rest of the run of railings will indicate the original detail, and this should be replicated for any repairs.

Original wrought iron backstay fixed in place by means of a bradded (riveted) pin

This backstay has been repaired by welding it back into position, which is not in keeping with the traditional techniques used to assemble this railing

Where cast iron backstays have fractured, the cause of their failure should be established and remedied. It may be necessary to re-stabilise the supporting wall and foundations of the railings. It may be necessary to recast the broken backstays, although brazing the broken sections together may be possible.

FRACTURED COPING STONES

Railings and rails were usually secured into masonry sockets using hot poured lead. If the iron begins to corrode within the socket, the developing corrosion, which has up to eight times the volume of iron, exerts pressure on the surrounding stone and can eventually fracture the stone.

If the coping stone has been fractured by corroding railings, the source of the problem should first be dealt with. The railings should be removed from the coping stone (either by chiselling out the lead holding them in place, or, as a last resort, by drilling around the base of the railings), thoroughly cleaned and repainted. If the fracture does not extend far, it may be possible to indent new stone using a lime mortar. Where damage is severe, it may be necessary to replace the entire stone. Any mortar used for repair should be lime-based, as cement mortar damages stone and brick due to its hardness and impermeability.

FIXING RAILINGS INTO MASONRY SOCKETS

Traditionally, railings were fixed in place by pouring molten lead into the masonry sockets. Lead is still the best method of securing ironwork in place, although this should only be undertaken by an experienced blacksmith. Caution is recommended, particularly if the stone is damp as this can cause the hot lead to spit.

Where the sockets have an unnaturally large diameter (which can occur when railings have been drilled out of the stone), new stone can be pieced in. Alternatively, while not an ideal solution, it may be preferred to use crushed stone in mortar to blend more naturally with the colour and texture of the stone coping. This method should only be used in exceptional circumstances and using a lime-based mortar. Resin should not be used to fix railings into masonry as it will cause damage to the stone due to its hardness and will be difficult to remove if problems arise at a later time.

Crushed stone mixed with mortar has been used to fix this ironwork into the masonry socket

A stone indent has been inserted to repair a fracture or widened socket

UNSTABLE FOUNDATIONS

Unstable foundations or shifting coping stones can cause distortion of ironwork and lead to sections of railing coming apart. The cause of any movement of the supporting wall should be identified and remedied before any repair works to iron railings are undertaken. It may be due to unstable foundations which can be consolidated. It may also be due to the loss of mortar which binds the wall together and that has been washed out by rain or high-pressure hosing. If this is the case, the walls should be re-pointed using a lime-based mortar.

CORROSION TO THE BASE OF A BAR

Corrosion frequently develops at the bases of bars due to the concentration of water flowing over these points from upper levels. When this corrosion material is removed, the bases of the bars are often found to have narrowed or 'wasted'. In many cases, there is still enough sound iron beneath the corrosion for it to remain structurally stable and consequently there is no need to replace it.

However, where corrosion has eroded too much of the bar, leading to instability, the corroded section should be removed and replaced with a new piece of wrought iron. Only the corroded section should be replaced. If bars are removed to carry out repair work, they should not be cut out above and below the rail. The hammered end of the bar, which fixes it in place on the underside of the rail, will need to be broken off in order to remove the bar and piece-in the new section of iron. When the repaired bar is reinstated, it should again be slotted through the holes in the rails as it was originally, and the end of the bar bradded on the underside of the rail to hold it in place. The new material should be forge-welded in place if work is being done off-site. Where work must be done in situ, it will be necessary to use modern welding techniques, taking care not to damage the adjacent stonework.

Bars do not necessarily need to be replaced when they have wasted at their base. Unless their condition is compromising the integrity of the ironwork, they can be left in place

Replacement bars should pierce through the rail rather than be welded to it (as shown above)

Posts from two different properties on Parnell Square, Dublin. While appearing to be severely corroded, much of the original ironwork in the lower example may remain intact beneath layers of paint and corrosion

CORRODED DECORATIVE SCROLLWORK

Many pillars and finials were embellished by finely-shaped scrollwork, demonstrating levels of craftsmanship rarely achieved today. Unfortunately, if they are not properly cleaned and painted, these details can be vulnerable to corrosion. This risk is compounded by their shape, which will often act as a water trap.

Often, the nose (or centre point) of these scrolls has corroded severely, although the rest of the scroll may be sound. All too often, the entire scroll has been removed and replaced with a clumsy, ill-formed scroll, which has been poorly welded in place. This damages the appearance of the ironwork and the longevity of the repair. In many cases, the entire scroll does not need to be discarded at all. Only the corroded section should be removed and replaced. The rest of the scroll should be retained and new material pieced-in to match. Very often it is possible to find properties in the vicinity that retain the same, or similar, feature which can provide enough information for a blacksmith to replicate the detail.

DISMANTLING AND RE-ASSEMBLING WROUGHT IRONWORK

When wrought iron railings need to be dismantled and removed to a workshop for repairs, it may be necessary to break or cut the pins, bradded ends of bars, or mortice-and-tenon joints holding the ironwork together. When the ironwork is to be re-assembled, new wrought iron should be pieced-in so that these joints and details can be re-formed.

It is particularly important to match the joining methods used by the original craftsperson. Details such as collars, rivets, and bars should be replicated so that repairs are in keeping with the original ironwork. Welding is not an appropriate substitute for collars, mortice-and-tenon joints, or rivets. Where sections of iron were traditionally joined together using forge welding, this method should also be used for their repair. However, where modern welding is unavoidable, a skilled blacksmith should be able to use modern welding techniques to create a visually acceptable repair. In general, modern welding should be discouraged as it builds in the potential for future galvanic corrosion due to the use of dissimilar metals.

CAST IRON RAILING PANELS AND BALCONIES: FRACTURES AND MISSING SECTIONS

Cast iron corrodes and becomes damaged in slightly different ways to wrought iron. Because it is a hard and brittle material, it will only accommodate a limited amount of movement or pressure before fracturing. Corroding wrought iron raggles (pointed spikes) within hollow finials can cause the finial to crack. The movement of foundations or impact damage can also cause shattering.

Where sections of cast iron panels have fractured, it may be possible to recast the section that is missing and fix it in place either by threaded bars or by brazing. However, it may be more feasible to recast the entire panel. Welding new sections in place is generally not recommended. Strap repairs should only be used as an emergency measure to stabilise ironwork until it can be repaired properly. New cast iron panels should be fixed in place using traditional detailing to match the existing adjoining panels.

Corrosion between the gate frame and slam bar is common

2. Gates

The conservation officer in the local authority should be consulted before making alterations to railings or gates. Works such as inserting new gates, widening existing gateways and automating gates may be subject to planning permission.

GATES THAT HAVE SEIZED OR WON'T OPEN PROPERLY

Gates may not function properly for a number of reasons including: rising ground levels; gate pillars that are not plumb (that are leaning); wearing of the gudgeon or heel cup (the shoe that the gate frame sits into in the ground in order to pivot); distortion of the gate through use or slamming; and loosening of the system securing the gate to a gate pillar. The cause of the problem will need to be identified before a repair can be planned.

CORROSION OF THE GATE'S SLAM BAR

A common problem with gates is that the slam bar (the flat section of wrought iron on the frame), or the section of iron behind it, begins to corrode. Slam bars will buckle or fracture as corrosion develops. The slam bar should be removed, cleaned, and reshaped and any corrosion from the underlying ironwork thoroughly removed. Both surfaces should be painted before the slam bar is replaced.

INSERTING A NEW GATE

Inappropriate repairs and alterations are likely to reduce the value and appeal of original features therefore the decision to alter existing ironwork should be made with care. Crudely-made mild steel gates that have been welded together can be an eyesore and will detract from the appearance of existing ironwork. New gates should be designed in accordance with the proportions, detailing and design of the original ironwork. It may be possible to form the new gate using the section of railings that it is to replace. New gateposts should not be attached to the original railings by welding. A competent blacksmith will be able to advise on a more traditional assembly method.

This replacement gate has been inserted sensitively and has been designed to tie in with the proportions and design of the original railings

WIDENING GATES

If wrought iron gates are to be widened, new sections should not be welded in place but sympathetically attached using traditional jointing details. This will improve the appearance and corrosion resistance of the gate. If cast iron gates are to be widened, normal modern welding methods are unlikely to be effective; brazing may be a more successful option.

AUTOMATING DRIVEWAY GATES

Any alterations to traditional ironwork should be done as unobtrusively as possible. Electronic arms should not be welded into position. Bolts are a more practical solution, although this will cause damage to the original ironwork. Cast iron gates are heavier than modern mild steel ones. It is therefore important to know the weight of the gate so that the appropriate system (such systems have weight ratings, measured in kilograms) can be installed. It is important first to establish what the implications will be for the historic ironwork before deciding to undertake this type of work.

3. Balconies, balconettes and window guards

The maintenance and repair of iron balconies is particularly important due to their location and the likelihood of people standing on them. There is also the potential danger of sections falling from them and injuring people below. Balconies should be regularly inspected to ensure that they are safe and in sound condition, which may require the services of a structural engineer. Floors of iron or stone, supporting brackets, and the masonry or brick sockets into which they are inserted should be inspected regularly to check for signs of decay or damage. The repair techniques for balconies are broadly the same as for railings as outlined above.

Due to their position and the potential for injuring people below, balconies and balconettes should be periodically inspected to ensure that they are secure

It is particularly important to ensure that all elements of a balcony are sound and secure to prevent injury to people stepping onto the balcony, or standing beneath it

4. Rainwater goods

Rainwater goods (gutters, downpipes, hoppers, etc) perform an important function by carrying rainwater away from a building. If gutters, hoppers, and drains are not inspected and cleaned annually they can become blocked, causing water to back-up. Blockages are likely to cause water to seep into the building, either through the roof or through moisture-soaked walls. This can lead not only to cosmetic damage, but to the decay of the building fabric.

Rainwater goods such as gutters, hoppers, and downpipes should be inspected at least twice a year to ensure that they are clear of blockages. As with any other type of external ironwork, they should be painted at least once every five years

Annual inspections should be carried out to make sure that rainwater goods are performing well. Problems such as leaks and blockages may be easier to spot during heavy rainfall. Rainwater goods, particularly gutters and hoppers, should be cleaned out at least twice a year, once in the spring and again in the late autumn after the leaves have fallen. Wire balloons and leaf guards can be fixed in place to help prevent blockages. Drains at the base of downpipes should also be inspected regularly and cleared when necessary to avoid water seeping into the building from ground level.

Cast iron rainwater goods should be periodically cleaned and repainted to prevent corrosion developing. Corrosion can usually be removed using a wire brush and sandpaper before new paint is applied. Care should be taken to paint the difficult-to-reach areas (such as the backs of downpipes) as these can be prone to corrosion. This can be difficult to do thoroughly due to their location but is a necessary task.

The collars that fix downpipes to the building façade (sometimes referred to as holderbats) and the bolts holding them to a wall can be prone to corrosion. These should be kept in good working order to avoid sections of downpipe becoming misaligned or loosened from the building. Where sections of downpipe are missing or have become detached, they should be repaired as soon as possible.

If downpipes become blocked in winter, the trapped water may become frozen and fracture the pipe. In such cases the pipe will need to be replaced. Replacement cast iron downpipes are readily available and many builders' merchants will have a selection in stock.

Decorative sections that have become too damaged to repair may need to be replaced. Foundries specialising in traditional casting have large stocks of patterns and may have a pattern to match the original.

Gutter brackets are easy to overlook but are often quite decorative. These can be made of either wrought iron or cast iron. Where these have been lost, mild steel brackets are not an appropriate substitute due to their poor corrosion resistance and the risk of galvanic corrosion. New brackets should match the originals in design and material. If this is not possible, stainless steel brackets may be used as replacements. Missing cast iron brackets should be replaced with new cast iron replicas.

5. Finials and weathervanes

The repair techniques for finials and weathervanes are largely the same as the repair techniques for railings. Both finials and weathervanes most commonly lose individual arms. If they are made of wrought iron, a new section can be forged and fire-welded into place. For cast iron pieces, it should be possible to have a pattern made for the missing section, which can be recast and either pinned or brazed in place.

Structural Ironwork

It is impossible in a publication of this size to discuss the repair and conservation of structural components in any detail. The topic is examined at length in Historic Scotland's publication *Scottish Iron Structures* which is essential reading for anyone working on large-scale projects involving ironwork and its advice is applicable to similar structures in Ireland. Nevertheless, most of the repair techniques and approaches to repair for decorative ironwork can be applied to the repair and conservation of structural ironwork, although the degree of relevance will vary from project to project. When planning the repair of structural ironwork, the advice of an architect or engineer with conservation expertise should be sought. It is important to balance the needs of conservation and structural performance, and a specialist with a sympathetic approach to historic structures will be essential for the successful completion of the project.

One of the primary concerns in projects of this kind will naturally be to ensure that the structure is stable and safe. When dealing with historic structures that have deteriorated over time, the temptation is often great to replace the original ironwork entirely in order to satisfy this concern. However, this is usually unnecessary, although a degree of imagination and ingenuity is sometimes required to devise ways of retaining as much of the original historic fabric as possible without compromising the integrity and safety of the structure. Any newly-introduced supporting ironwork should be self-documenting, in that it reads as not being part of the historic construction. Date stamping is a useful means of identifying newly-introduced ironwork.

Corrosion is often localised to vulnerable points, such as areas where water or condensation can collect (especially if there are leaks). As with smaller items of ironwork, it is always preferable to retain sound material rather than replace an entire component. While any repair methodology will need to ensure the structural strength and performance of the component, in many cases repair techniques (such as plating) can be used to reinforce or strengthen the original fabric. Other methods, like welding and metal stitching, allow new material to be joined to existing ironwork where corroded material has had to be removed. If original components are replaced entirely, little or nothing of the historic character of the structure will remain. Additionally, original features such as jointing techniques (often particularly interesting in early iron structures) will be lost. Such features are historically important and should be preserved wherever possible.

The Ha'penny Bridge (originally Wellington Bridge but officially named the Liffey Bridge from 1836) in Dublin, underwent repair and conservation work in 2001. As it is believed to be the earliest cast iron bridge built in Ireland, it was particularly important to retain as much of the historic fabric as possible. A condition assessment showed that while the original superstructure was sound, the cast iron railings enclosing the walkway had failed at a number of points, posing a safety risk to the public. Various tests were conducted on the original fabric to establish its exact strength, which showed that the original cast iron was stronger than had been assumed. This scientific testing prior to devising a repair methodology enabled a compromise to be reached whereby 85% of the original railings were retained rather than replaced.

Dating to 1816, the Ha'penny Bridge is the oldest cast iron bridge in Ireland. It is also one of the earliest cast iron bridges ever made. Its parts were fabricated by the famous English firm Coalbrookdale, also responsible for making the first cast iron bridge in the world, which still stands at Ironbridge, Shropshire, England

Whatever the structure, one of the most commonly encountered problems is likely to be corrosion of fixings. Wrought iron fixings were often used on cast iron structures which in many cases caused galvanic corrosion to develop. This is a particularly important consideration in the maintenance of ironwork fountains. While the exterior may appear to be in reasonable condition, the interior (which often remains wet for more prolonged periods of time) may have suffered more severe corrosion leading to a significant loss of fixings. Where fixings are to be replaced, stainless steel or phosphor bronze are the preferred materials. New fixings should be isolated wherever possible from the surrounding ironwork by means of an inert insulating material such as nylon. Screws and other fixings should be tightened with caution, preferably by hand, rather than over-tightening with pneumatic or torque tools, to avoid causing stress fractures to surrounding ironwork.

The conservation of adjacent materials such as tiled floors, supporting masonry or glazing should not be overlooked when dealing with larger projects. Traditional plain glass is an often-overlooked aspect of glasshouse conservation. Many types of traditional conservatory glass are no longer manufactured and the retention and conservation of existing glazing in such structures will merit consideration.

This finely-made circular conservatory was designed and erected at Castlebridge House, County Wexford by James Pierce of Mill Road Iron Works, Wexford. In addition to its iron structure, it contains a 10-tier iron display stand for plants at its centre

Some safety issues

GETTING READY

Wear the right clothes when carrying out maintenance or repair works. Wear shoes, or boots, with a good grip. Don't wear clothes with trailing pieces or cords as these may catch and cause you to fall.

WORKING AT A HEIGHT

Carrying out repair works or maintenance inspections at a height is hazardous. If you feel don't feel safe, or are nervous working at a height, then get professional help with the work.

Using ladders is a major safety issue. Avoid working on ladders in poor weather conditions such as windy, wet, or icy conditions. It is always safest not to work alone. You should have someone competent with you to hold the ladder. Take care of people below when working at a height to avoid injuries caused by falling or thrown objects. Always use a ladder that is in good condition and of the correct height. Make sure it is secure, angled correctly with the top resting against a solid surface, not a gutter or a fascia. When climbing ladders make sure you have both hands free. Always work so you can have one hand on the ladder at all times, have a good handhold, and don't overreach.

With many buildings that are larger or higher than an average dwelling, it may not be safe for an untrained person to carry out even the simplest maintenance or repair tasks. In fact, it is not advisable for any untrained person to work from ladders above one-storey high. You could consider hiring, or investing in, a properly-designed mobile scaffold tower or a mobile elevated working platform.

For further information on the safety issues of working at a height, see the Health & Safety Authority's publication: *Code of Practice for Safety in Roofwork.*

WORKING WITH LEAD PAINT

Lead paint was the traditional high-quality finish for metalwork and is extremely long-lasting. Its use continued until the 1960s. These paints used linseed oil as the binder and white lead as the pigment. The appearance of the painted finish ages in a characteristic way which cannot be replicated by modern paints.

There are serious health risks associated with lead paints where a painted surface is unsound or is disturbed. Test kits can be used which give an indication of the presence of lead paint. For absolute certainty as to the presence of lead paint, specialist laboratory testing should be carried out. The fumes created when applying lead paint or burning it off and the dust resulting from sanding it down are particularly hazardous. Sound lead paint should be left in place and, if necessary, can be sealed by over-painting with a modern paint. If the need arises, it should only be removed and/or reapplied in compliance with all relevant safety standards.

Lead paints containing white lead are no longer readily available to buy in this country. Their importation can be licensed on application to the Health & Safety Authority for use in certain historic buildings including protected structures and recorded monuments. There are no restrictions on the use of red lead paint, the traditional primer used on ironwork, which is still widely available.

5. Planning Repairs

The aim of any repair project should always be to carry out the minimum level of intervention and to retain as much of the original material as possible. This section sets out the steps involved in the repair and conservation of architectural ironwork. These steps can generally be applied to both small and large-scale projects:

> Finding the right contractor

> Assessing and recording the condition of ironwork

> Analysing existing coatings and paint layers

> Research

> Deciding whether repairs will be carried out in-situ or off-site

> Devising a repair methodology

The explanation of these steps is followed by more practical and specific information concerning cleaning and repair techniques and their application to specific problems. By following these steps, it should be possible for a building owner or specifier and the contractor to agree on a repair system that is sympathetic to the original ironwork.

Finding the right contractor

The craft skills to carry out competent repairs to historic ironwork still exist in Ireland, although the number of skilled practitioners is diminishing year by year. There are currently no apprenticeships or formal training in traditional blacksmithing or founding techniques available in Ireland. As experienced craftspeople with knowledge of traditional techniques retire, there are few entering the industry with the same understanding of traditional techniques to take their place. It is therefore important to select a craftsperson carefully to ensure that they have the relevant experience for the project in hand.

BLACKSMITHS

Today, the term 'fabricator' is often confused with that of 'blacksmith'. While both crafts deal with iron and steel, the skills used differ considerably. Traditionally, blacksmiths served a long apprenticeship and were trained to work iron without the use of modern welding techniques. Fabricators are not trained in traditional blacksmithing techniques. They generally work with steel and it is unlikely that they will be equipped with the relevant expertise to carry out repair work to traditional wrought ironwork.

A blacksmith skilled in traditional techniques should always be used for the repair of traditional ironwork. Be sure to view an example of repair work that they have done in the past and, for larger jobs, always request test pieces before any work is undertaken to historic ironwork, particularly where scrollwork or other fine detailing is to be made or repaired.

IRON FOUNDERS

The methods and materials used to mould and cast ironwork greatly affect the level of detail that can be achieved. All castings begin with a pattern that is used to make the mould. A poorly-made pattern will result in a poor quality casting and so it is important to find a skilled pattern-maker who has experience in producing patterns for decorative cast ironwork. Sadly, this is a skill which is in decline.

Modern casting techniques, which use chemically-setting sand, are unsuited to delicate ornamental cast ironwork as they result in a poorer quality of detail. Therefore it is important to insist on the use of traditional green sand moulds. This method may be slightly more expensive because it is more time-consuming, but produces a far better finish on decorative castings. Only one foundry remaining in Ireland makes castings in the traditional way, although a number of such foundries exist in the UK.

It is advisable to check patterns before castings are made. Castings should also be checked before they are accepted to make sure that they have been cast and finished properly.

Bear in mind that a foundry usually will not install the ironwork that it produces – a separate blacksmith is generally required to do this work. A foundry will often subcontract this work. Equally, many blacksmiths will source castings on behalf of the client.

GENERAL CONTRACTORS AND SUBCONTRACTING

There are many firms that specialise in the conservation of metalwork, particularly high-status or large-scale items. Before placing a contract, it is important to establish whether a firm has the appropriate in-house skills or can subcontract suitably-experienced craftspeople such as blacksmiths where required. Examples of previous projects should be sought and the projects visited in person if possible. In the case of ironwork, it is not sufficient to rely on photographs when assessing the quality of previous work. Detailing such as joints, fixings and how well the paint has been applied need to be assessed on site.

PROFESSIONAL SERVICES

For larger projects, such as the repair of fountains and bandstands, or where the repair to ironwork will coincide with repairs to other parts of a building, the services of an appropriately-qualified and experienced architect or similar professional are recommended to co-ordinate and oversee work. Where works are to structural elements such as beams, trusses, or columns, the advice of a suitably-qualified structural engineer should be sought.

Assessing and recording the condition of ironwork

Before embarking on repairs, the contractor should assess the ironwork's condition as this will determine the degree of intervention and type of repairs required. The ironwork should be photographed to record its appearance and condition before any works start, and should also be measured. An accurate, measured drawing of the ironwork is particularly important where ironwork is to be removed off-site for repairs so that it can be accurately reinstated.

Surrounding materials such as stone, brick or timber should also be considered at this stage so that measures can be put in place for their protection, and any necessary repair work can be programmed. If sections of stone need to be replaced or indented, time may need to be built into the repair programme to allow for the ordering and preparation of the new stone. Colour-coded or annotated drawings and photographs are a useful and clear way of showing where and what type of repair work is proposed. A record of the condition, position, and appearance of ironwork prior to intervention or dismantling is invaluable and should be considered essential for large-scale or ornate ironwork. Where ironwork is to be dismantled, every element should be numbered using brass or aluminium tags that correspond to a numbered drawing of the ironwork so that every element can be accurately reinstated in its original location.

For domestic-scaled ironwork such as railings, the contractor should be able to produce a simple measured drawing and photographic survey. The recording and assessment of larger or more complex examples of ironwork will require the services of a suitably qualified and experienced architect, surveyor or engineer as appropriate, particularly if the ironwork is performing a structural function.

Attaching metal tags to ironwork as it is dismantled (numbered to correspond with a measured survey drawing) is essential for tracking repairs and for correct reinstatement (Image courtesy of Historic Scotland)

Accurately recording the position of each element of ironwork is essential and enables ironwork to be reinstated correctly after repairs. The railings illustrated above appear to have been reinstated in the wrong positions, resulting in a misalignment of the railing feet and original corresponding sockets in the coping stones

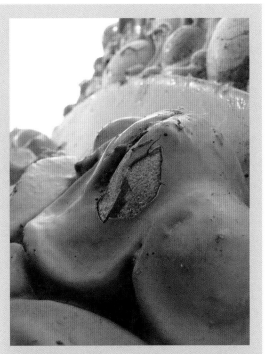

Original decorative schemes, such as gilding, can be hidden under layers of modern paint (Image courtesy of Historic Scotland)

Analysing existing coatings and paint layers

Layers of paint accumulate over the years and later paint may conceal early or original coatings. For ironwork of any significance it is advisable to take paint samples which can be professionally analysed under a microscope. These may reveal original or earlier colour schemes and the types of coatings which were applied. See also page 16.

For smaller projects, this need not be an expensive undertaking. A feathered cut into ironwork can also be an effective means of revealing consecutive layers of colour. But it needs to be borne in mind that different coats – primer, build coat, and top coat – were often different colours, making it difficult to recognise which layer was the finished appearance of the paintwork. Primers can sometimes be easily distinguished as they were often a red colour, particularly where traditional red lead paint was used. Some paint colours will have changed from their original appearance under the influence of sunlight and other factors.

Analysis of paint scrapings can reveal much about earlier decorative schemes. Even viewing a section through the paint layers with the naked eye can often reveal useful information about underlying coats of paint

Research

For ironwork of any significance or scale, further historical research should be carried out to discover more about its history and origin, although this can equally be carried out for more common ironwork. Makers' names and other marks such as supplier stamps or registration stamps can often be found on both large and small-scale ironwork on flat surfaces such as bottom rails, gate slam bars, or column and post bases. Blacksmiths often stamped ironwork, particularly on the slam bars of gates. Similarly, cast iron manufacturers, would cast their name into ironwork.

Registration marks will give the year in which a particular design was registered

Street directories are a useful reference tool – if the name of a blacksmith has been identified on the ironwork it is often possible to trace where, and during which period, the blacksmith was working. This will allow the ironwork to be roughly dated. It is also occasionally possible to find a particular design in a manufacturer's catalogue, (although sadly, few Irish manufacturers' catalogues survive). Catalogues survive for J & C McGloughlin & Co. and Kennan & Sons in the National Archives and the Irish Architectural Archive. Much cast ironwork found in Ireland was imported from companies in England and Scotland, and there is a greater abundance of their catalogues in existence. A few are kept at the Irish Architectural Archive and can be consulted there. Original design drawings may also survive, particularly in the case of bespoke ironwork for public buildings and churches. Detailing and the mode of assembly can also give clues as to the date of ironwork. Old photographs from local libraries or national archive collections can be invaluable in identifying the design of missing elements of ironwork.

Assessment, recording and research should:

> Establish whether the ironwork is cast, wrought or a mixture of materials

> Establish how it was originally assembled

> Establish the origin and maker of the ironwork where possible

> Evaluate the significance of the ironwork, both in terms of the object itself, and its context and surroundings

> Identify problems of deterioration and their causes

> Identify any non-original repairs and interventions

> Indicate which areas require intervention and which can be left as they are

> Highlight aspects that are of particular importance, interest or vulnerability

> Identify earlier colour schemes where evidence remains

Deciding whether repair work should be done in situ or off-site

Deciding whether to repair ironwork on- or off-site can be problematic. Where only minor, localised areas of corrosion have occurred and minimal amounts of work are required, the decision to repair ironwork in situ can be a relatively easy one. However, where ironwork needs to be cleaned thoroughly to remove more serious corrosion, it is virtually impossible to remove all rust without dismantling the ironwork and removing it off-site. By cleaning ironwork in situ, small areas of corrosion are likely to remain in joints and cracks. These will continue to develop and may damage and stain new paintwork. Repairs are also more difficult to carry out in situ. Traditional fire welding, for example, is only possible in a workshop.

Cleaning and repairing ironwork in situ has the added disadvantage that it is impossible to control the environment. Where iron has been cleaned back to bare metal, it needs to be absolutely dry before it is painted. Rain, dew and even high relative humidity can cause moisture to soak into the iron. If paint is applied to damp bare metal, the evaporating moisture will be trapped beneath the paint when the temperature rises. This will cause corrosion to begin. Removing ironwork off-site allows it to be cleaned thoroughly and painted under perfect conditions which will ensure the effective performance of the new paint. Dismantling and thorough cleaning may also reveal further problems that might not be noticed where work is done in situ. Nevertheless, cleaning and repairing ironwork in situ can have its advantages. Removing ironwork from coping stones can be difficult and has the potential to damage stonework. Also, dismantling wrought iron railings usually necessitates breaking the riveted ends holding the bases of each bar into the lower rail, although these can be repaired.

The decision to repair in situ or off-site will usually require some form of compromise and must be made on a case-by-case basis. As a general rule of thumb, if only minor painting and/or repairs are required, then it may be feasible to carry out the work in situ. If work is to be conducted in situ, surrounding materials such as stone and render should be adequately protected so that they are not stained by any dust or corrosion run-off as the metal is cleaned. However, where corrosion or damage of the ironwork is severe or where it is intended to clean the ironwork back to bare metal, the most effective way of doing this is usually off-site. Issues of public safety may also influence the decision to carry out repairs off-site.

Devising a repair methodology

Repair work needs to be planned carefully. Once a condition assessment has been carried out and before any work is begun, the contractor should be asked to supply a comprehensive method statement.

The method statement should outline:

> Whether work will be done in situ or off-site

> How members of the public and adjacent materials will be protected from work in situ

> If ironwork is to be removed, how the contractor proposes to remove it and protect it during transportation

> What effect removal will have on adjacent materials such as coping stones

> Where the ironwork will be stored off-site (does the contractor have adequate and secure facilities?)

> How, and to what degree, the ironwork will be cleaned (back to bare metal, or just back to sound paint)

> If blast cleaning is proposed, what medium will be used

> What repair work is proposed

> Which sections of iron are to be repaired

> How repairs will be done

> What sections are to be replaced

> What material and techniques will be used for replacement material

> What design is proposed for replacement material

> What method will be used to insert new material into the existing ironwork

> What assembly techniques will be applied

> Where appropriate, what type of fixings are proposed (mild steel, stainless steel or bronze), how they will be isolated from surrounding ironwork, and what fillers will be used

> What paint system is proposed and how will it be applied

For larger projects, the methodology may need to be reviewed and amended once the ironwork has been cleaned, as this can often reveal further problems that were not visible during the initial inspection. The contractor should be specific about what areas of ironwork will be repaired and exactly what techniques and materials will be used. All of these factors will affect the longevity of any repairs. A coloured or marked-up drawing can be useful to clearly indicate and explain the proposed repair work.

Historic buildings and the law

Under Part IV of the *Planning and Development Act 2000,* buildings which form part of the architectural heritage can be protected either by being designated a protected structure or by being located within an architectural conservation area.

Where a building is a protected structure (or has been proposed for protection) or is located within an architectural conservation area, the usual exemptions from requirements for planning permission do not apply. In the case of a protected structure any works, whether internal or external, which would materially affect its character will require planning permission. Legal protection also extends to other structures and features associated with a protected structure such as outbuildings, boundary walls, paving, railings and the like. In an architectural conservation area, any works which would affect the character of the area also require planning permission. This may include works to ironwork such as railings and gates. Owners and occupiers of protected structures have a responsibility to maintain their buildings and not to damage them or allow them to fall into decay through neglect.

A notice was sent to every owner and occupier of a protected structure when the building first became protected but subsequent owners and occupiers will not have been notified. If you are not sure of the status of your building, check the Record of Protected Structures in the Development Plan for the area. If your building is a protected structure, or if it is located in an architectural conservation area, your planning authority will be able to tell you what this means for your particular property.

As an owner or occupier of a protected structure, you are entitled to ask the planning authority to issue a Declaration which will guide you in identifying works that would, or would not, require planning permission. Maintenance and repair works, if carried out in line with good conservation practice and the guidance contained within this booklet, will generally not require planning permission. If you are in any doubt about particular proposed works, you should contact the conservation officer in your local authority for advice.

For general advice on planning issues relating to architectural heritage, a publication entitled *Architectural Heritage Protection Guidelines for Planning Authorities* (2004) is available from the Government Publications Sales Office or can be downloaded from www.environ.ie

6. Common Repair Techniques

Most of the ironwork that survives in Ireland displays a high level of craftsmanship that is rarely matched today. It is therefore important that repairs respect the quality, character and detailing of historic ironwork. There are many repair techniques that can be used, both traditional and non-traditional, although some are more appropriate and successful than others. These include:

> Forge welding (also known as fire welding)

> Modern welding techniques

> Braze welding

> Pinning

> Stitch repairs

> Epoxy repairs

> Strap repairs

> Plate repairs

> The use of concrete

> Replicating wrought and cast ironwork

Ideally, ironwork should be repaired using the same material as the original. The choice of material will not only affect the ironwork visually, but will also impact on the longevity of the repair. The principal aim should always be to choose a material that will have the least impact and cause the least damage to the ironwork in the future. Nevertheless, for a variety of reasons, a number of alternative materials are commonly used, and compromise may be necessary in particular circumstances.

Repair methods should be selected with care as inappropriate techniques can be damaging to ironwork in the long run. Poor quality repairs, resulting from either a lack of training and skills or bad practice, can detrimentally affect not only the appearance of ironwork, but also its longevity and resistance to corrosion.

Repairs should be sympathetic to the design and traditional detailing of ironwork unlike this repair which is damaging to the appearance of the railings, will damage the stone coping and is likely to fail

Small details, such as joint and assembly techniques, fixings and the shape or surface quality of forged (shaped by hammering) or cast details should not be overlooked as these are the aspects which give traditional ironwork its unique appeal and distinctive character.

When planning repairs, however, a compromise can be necessary to achieve the right balance between retaining as much of the original material as possible and stabilising the ironwork.

FORGE WELDING (ALSO KNOWN AS FIRE WELDING)

Wrought iron was traditionally forge or fire welded. This is a process whereby iron is put on the hearth of the forge, brought to a high heat, then joined to another section of heated iron by hammering the two together to form a seamless join. A blacksmith will forge wrought iron when it has been heated to varying temperatures in the forge, using either hand tools or a mechanical hammer. Shaping wrought iron or mild steel in this way takes great skill. Ideally, any weld repairs to wrought iron should be done in this way. The join will be unobtrusive and in keeping with the rest of the ironwork and will not be a weak point for the development of corrosion. Only wrought iron, which is malleable, can be shaped by forging. Cast iron is a brittle material and would shatter under the hammer.

A blacksmith at work

Cast iron cannot be forge welded, but can be welded using modern welding techniques. Cast iron can however, be difficult to weld and this type of repair should only be carried out by an experienced contractor. Cast iron weld repairs are often unsuccessful. Because the rod used to form the weld joint will be a different type of metal, the weld may fail due to the stresses exerted as the two metals cool at different rates. Traditionally, cast iron was assembled without the use of any welding at all, usually by means of lugs, grooves, pins, and bolts. More mechanical means of repairing cast iron, such as pinning, are usually preferable to welding.

MODERN WELDING TECHNIQUES

Modern welding techniques became widespread from the 1930s and should generally be avoided for the repair of traditional ironwork. Modern welding uses a rod of a different metal to form the weld joint, which automatically builds in a defect that may lead to galvanic corrosion in the future. Additionally, weld splatter left around the weld joint can act as a moisture trap and cause corrosion to begin.

However in some cases, the use of modern welding techniques is unavoidable, but it should only be considered as a last resort. For example, it might be the case that ironwork must be repaired in situ, which eliminates the possibility of traditional forge welding. A skilled blacksmith may be able to use modern welding techniques to produce a visually acceptable welded joint. Rods with a high nickel content are preferable. Where pinning or other traditional repairs are not possible, brazing (detailed below) may be a more successful alternative.

While modern welding techniques are not ideally suited to traditional ironwork, a skilled craftsperson may be able to apply modern welding to repairs to a level that is visually acceptable. The finial on the left has been forge welded and hammered down to a point, while the finial on the right has been electric arc welded and then hammered into a point in the traditional way

Poorly-finished weld joints can be disfiguring to traditional and new iron and steelwork alike

BRAZE WELDING

Brazing is a form of welding that uses an alloy rod, commonly brass or bronze, and is often the most successful method of welding cast iron. This is a specialist technique and should only be carried out by an experienced craftsperson.

PINNING

Pinning is a particularly useful repair technique for cast iron that has fractured, although it may not be suitable for repairing structural elements. Fractured sections can be joined together by drilling one or more threaded holes into each fractured face and screwing them together using a threaded stainless steel bar. The fractured faces should be painted prior to reassembly and the threaded bar coated in a layer of wet paint as it is screwed into place. Pinning may not be possible where the section is too narrow, in which case brazing may be a more practical alternative.

STITCH REPAIRS

Stitching involves drilling a series of holes along the length of the fracture and then drilling more holes perpendicular to the fracture. A series of metal 'keys' or stitches is then inserted into the holes across the fracture to hold the fractured sections together. The advantage of such a repair is that it will allow much of the original fabric to be retained and results in a self-documenting repair that will allow future owners to see where work has been undertaken. Additionally, it may be accepted as a structural repair by a structural engineer where a weld repair might not. However, there are drawbacks in that the fracture remains and may act as a water trap and the visual appearance of a stitch repair may not always be acceptable.

EPOXY REPAIRS

Epoxy repairs involve the use of epoxy resin to build up sections or fill cavities and depressions in the iron. As with many repair techniques, the use of epoxy requires a compromise to the principle of like-for-like repairs. However, it is a reversible method of repair (epoxy can be blasted off ironwork) and is useful for re-profiling corroded, pitted sections of ironwork so that they shed water, particularly where galvanic corrosion has occurred. An added advantage is that the epoxy will isolate dissimilar metals from one another where this type of corrosion has occurred. For a successful epoxy repair, the iron surface must be thoroughly clean and dry before application.

STRAP REPAIRS

Strap repairs can be unsightly and their use is generally not recommended. However, they can be an effective short term, emergency measure to secure damaged ironwork until it can be correctly repaired. Straps should never be attached by drilling through the ironwork itself. Instead, two straps should 'sandwich' the iron and be bolted to each other.

Strap repairs can be visually intrusive and detract from the appearance of ironwork

PLATE REPAIRS

Plate repairs involve pinning a section of steel to ironwork. It can be a useful repair technique, particularly for fractured columns. In such cases a steel tube can be positioned within the hollow of the column and pinned through the column wall. The disadvantage of this technique is that it is non-reversible and damages the historic fabric, due to the need to drill holes. There is also a potential for galvanic corrosion unless the plate is isolated from the iron by an inert insulating material such as nylon. As with many other repair techniques, the merits of this repair need to be balanced against the potential loss of, or damage to, the historic fabric.

THE USE OF CONCRETE

Concrete is often used to stabilise corroding bases of railing shafts or to fill damaged newel posts. It can be very damaging to ironwork and is not recommended for repairs to historic ironwork. Not only will such repairs damage the ironwork itself, but they are also likely to damage surrounding masonry. The concrete itself can corrode iron due to its alkalinity and, because it shrinks as it sets, it is likely to leave gaps between it and the metal, which in turn create moisture traps. The concrete may crack over time, drawing in and holding moisture against the iron and causing corrosion that is hidden from view. Such repairs are also visually damaging to the character of ironwork and can detract from the appearance of any adjacent stonework.

Concrete is not an appropriate material for the repair of ironwork, particularly in combination with stone

REPLICATING WROUGHT AND CAST IRONWORK

Where new sections need to be inserted into existing ironwork, it is always preferable to use the same material (wrought iron or cast iron) so that new material will be in keeping with the character of the rest of the ironwork and to prevent the risk of galvanic corrosion.

Traditional techniques should be used to shape and assemble new sections, which can be date-stamped at an inconspicuous location to distinguish them from the original material. New wrought iron or mild steel replacements should always be shaped by an experienced blacksmith, and new castings should be cast using the traditional green sand method. The use of traditional techniques by experienced craftspeople will make all the difference to the quality and appearance of replacement elements.

REPLICATING WROUGHT IRONWORK

Where wrought iron repairs are concerned, as much of the original fabric as possible should be retained. New wrought iron is no longer available in Europe and there is no known commercial source of the material in the world. A limited amount of recycled wrought iron is available from a single supplier in the UK. The skills to create wrought ironwork to the same quality as that produced up until the early twentieth century are also in decline. It is therefore vital to retain as much of the original ironwork as possible.

However, wrought iron can be expensive and difficult to obtain, and may at times be beyond the budget of homeowners. Where a substitute material is to be

It is important to choose an experienced craftsperson to avoid inappropriate repairs. The replacement scroll in the lower image has been crudely formed and bears little resemblance to the finely-crafted original feature on a neighbouring property in the top image

used, stainless steel (which can be joined mechanically or by welding) is preferable to mild steel due to its superior corrosion resistance (although it is harder to work by hammer).

Repairs that use mild steel may be less effective and are not likely to last as long as a similar repair using wrought iron and appropriate traditional detailing. In the long term, using mild steel for conservation work does not make sense. By saving in the short term, higher costs are likely to be incurred at a later date because of mild steel's inferior corrosion resistance and it should therefore only be used as a last resort. Mild steel has the added disadvantage of being manufactured according to the metric rather than the imperial measuring system which means that replacement mild steel bars for railings, for example, will not exactly match existing wrought iron bars. However, the reality is that wrought iron may be beyond the budget of many private individuals. The simplest solution in such cases is to carry out only those repairs that are absolutely necessary, for example where an element or missing element is causing or contributing to structural unsoundness. The condition of the existing ironwork may often be stabilised without replacing any of the historic wrought iron.

Where a different metal has to be used, it should be isolated wherever possible by an inert insulating material such as nylon sleeves or washers. Future maintenance should take special care to keep such areas well-painted to guard against corrosion.

REPLICATING CAST IRONWORK

New castings should be cast using the traditional green sand mould technique. Original ironwork should not be used as the pattern for making a mould as this is likely to reduce the sharpness of detail and surface quality of the resulting casting. Cast iron shrinks by approximately 1%, therefore the resulting casting would also be smaller than the original component it was meant to replicate. Original ironwork can instead be used as a reference or template for a new pattern to be made. Hand-carved timber patterns are preferable, although some foundries also make patterns out of different materials such as resin.

Patterns should be checked before the castings are made to ensure that the surface finish and detailing is of good quality. Once the castings have been made, they should be checked to ensure that any flashing (sharp edges of waste iron that can form around the joint line of the mould during casting) has been

removed and that the quality of the casting is good (for example, that the two halves of the casting align correctly) before being put in place.

It is advisable to inspect patterns before they are used for making castings to ensure that the detailing is accurate and that the surface finish is smooth (Image courtesy of Historic Scotland)

Castings should be checked before they are put in place to ensure that they are of acceptable quality. The casting illustrated above is deformed because the two halves of the mould were not aligned correctly during the casting process

Aluminium is not an appropriate substitute for grey cast iron

Grant aid

Conservation grants are available for the conservation and repair of protected structures and are administered by the planning authorities. You should contact the relevant one for guidance on whether the works you are planning are eligible for a grant and, if so, how to apply. These grants are not available for routine maintenance works, alterations or improvements. The type of works must fit within the schedule of priorities set out by the planning authority. In order for works to qualify for these grants, they must be carried out in line with good conservation practice. Repair work following the guidance set out in this booklet should be considered as satisfying this requirement.

Other bodies also provide grants for building conservation projects. These include the Heritage Council and the Irish Georgian Society. Their contact details are included elsewhere in this guide.

Tax incentives are available under Section 482 of the Taxes Consolidation Act 1997 for expenditure incurred on the repair, maintenance, or restoration of certain buildings or gardens determined to be of significant horticultural, scientific, historical, architectural or aesthetic interest. The building or garden must receive a determination from the Revenue Commissioners who must be satisfied that there is reasonable public access to the property. Application forms can be obtained from the Heritage Policy Unit, Department of the Environment, Heritage and Local Government.

7. Iron and Common Substitute Materials

There are many types of iron and steel, and while they may often appear to be similar superficially, each has a distinct set of characteristics. This is an important consideration when planning repairs to traditional ironwork. This chapter outlines how the most common types of iron, steel and their substitutes differ from one another so that an informed decision can be made when planning repairs.

Distinguishing wrought iron from cast iron

Before embarking on repairs, it is important to establish whether ironwork is made of cast iron, wrought iron or a mixture of materials as this will determine what course of action is required. One of the most frequently-encountered problems when looking at historic ironwork is determining whether it is made of wrought iron or cast iron. Issues also arise when distinguishing wrought iron from mild steel, which is commonly used to repair wrought iron. While it is usually possible for the trained eye to distinguish between wrought iron, cast iron and steel, scientific analysis may occasionally be required to confirm the material where visual identification is difficult.

Wrought iron

Wrought iron contains very little carbon and is fibrous in composition (similar to wood), due to the presence of long strands of slag. It is malleable (it is easily shaped by hammering and rolling) and ductile (it can be shaped by extrusion through dies to form wires). It is strong in tension and generally has good corrosion resistance. Because wrought iron contains relatively little carbon it is mechanically weaker than steel.

Wrought iron was formed by 'puddling' pig iron in a reverberatory furnace. This process involved re-melting the pig iron in a furnace which kept the iron and fuel separate. When the iron was molten it was constantly stirred, or 'rabbled', to expose as much of it as possible to the air so that carbon would be given off as gas, turning it into a relatively pure iron. Eventually the iron became thicker and spongy and could be rolled into a ball known as a 'bloom'. This was then hammered, or 'shingled', using a steam hammer to drive out molten

slag, and rolled into bars or sheets by passing the bloom through a rolling mill. The bloom was then chopped up, tied into a stack using wire, re-heated, hammered and rolled again. This process was repeated numerous times. The more often the process was repeated the better the quality of iron. Traditionally, wrought iron was classified as 'best', 'best best' or 'best best best' quality.

The last puddling furnace for producing wrought iron in England closed in 1974, and since then no wrought iron has been produced in Ireland, the UK, or the rest of Europe. Wrought iron is currently only available as recycled material and can be obtained from a single supplier in the UK. As a result, the cost of wrought iron can be up to ten times that of mild steel (its most common substitute), and sourcing wrought iron can take much longer. Because new wrought iron is no longer produced, it is a virtually irreplaceable material. Every effort should therefore be made to retain as much of it as possible. Despite the difficulties in obtaining the material, there are very real benefits to using wrought iron for repairs. First, using the same material eliminates the risk of galvanic corrosion which is caused by two dissimilar materials being placed beside each other. This is a common problem with mild steel repairs. In addition, wrought iron is generally considered to have excellent corrosion resistance – a repair using wrought iron will be a long lasting one.

Note the pin just below the top rail of these wrought iron railings which would have been used to hold the rail in place during the assembly of the railings in situ

IDENTIFYING WROUGHT IRON

Wrought iron was traditionally shaped by rolling and hammering it when hot. Both of these processes determine the types of shapes and designs that can be produced. Designs in wrought iron tend to be light and are usually composed of several individual pieces fitted together. Slight variations can often be discerned either in the overall pattern, or between similar individual elements within the pattern, as it is difficult to make any two handmade elements identical. One of the simplest ways of telling whether the bars of a gate or set of railings are wrought or cast iron is to look at the underside of the rails. Wrought iron bars pierce through rails and the bases of these bars are 'bradded' or 'riveted' (their ends are hammered into dome shapes) on the underside to hold them in place. Other sections of a wrought iron structure are typically held together using rivets, collars, mortice-and-tenon joints and other traditional methods based on joinery techniques. Wrought iron cannot be shaped by casting.

Delicate leaf-work is typical of wrought ironwork

A simple, nicely detailed vernacular wrought iron gate beside a farmhouse in Kerry. This gate has been made using hoop iron (some of which still lies close to the gate), using wrought iron pins and rivets. Hoop iron was usually used on wooden cartwheels, but was often re-cycled in this way when wheels were discarded. This gate has not been painted for many decades, yet its generally good condition illustrates the durability of wrought iron

Tapering scrolls are another common feature of wrought ironwork

Wrought iron was traditionally assembled by means such as forge welding, collars, scarf joints, and mortice-and-tenon joints

Cast iron

Grey cast iron is the form of iron most commonly found in eighteenth- and nineteenth-century cast iron structures and architectural ornamentation. It has a higher carbon content than wrought iron, which makes it harder and crystalline in composition. The crystalline nature of grey cast iron means that it is hard and strong in compression, but is also brittle. It will shatter rather than bend as the result of a sharp blow. It is made by re-melting pig iron in a furnace, skimming off the slag (waste material) which floats on the top, pouring it into a mould and allowing it to cool slowly.

An iron casting is made by using a pattern (traditionally carved out of wood) to create an impression in sand which then forms a mould. The mould is made in two halves and the pattern is often also made in two halves to facilitate this. Traditional moulding techniques use a specific type of sand known as green sand (a natural, round grained sand containing clay, which helps the mould to bind together without the aid of added chemicals while still remaining soft). The fine grain of green sand helps to create a smooth surface finish and enables a high level of detail to be captured in the casting. Once the desired impression is made in the sand, the pattern is removed and the two halves of the moulding box fastened together. Molten iron is then poured into the mould and allowed to cool before the mould is opened and the casting knocked out. Green sand moulds cannot be re-used because the sand remains soft at all times. Only the timber patterns can be reused. Modern moulding techniques use a sharp-grained sand which is set hard by means of chemicals, allowing the mould to be used a number of times. The drawback of this method is that the surface finish of castings is often rougher and less finely detailed than castings made by means of the traditional green sand mould process.

Because of its strength in compression and its hardness, grey cast iron was traditionally used for columns and other load-bearing structural elements, as well as for engineering parts and decorative castings such as railings and gates. Cast iron is still used to produce decorative ironwork and rainwater goods as well as items such as brake discs and engine blocks in cars. Its strength and durability make it ideally suited to these purposes. Grey cast iron is still widely available today from iron foundries. However, there is currently only one foundry in Ireland that casts iron in the traditional way using green sand moulds. A number of foundries that cast in the traditional way are in operation in the UK.

Pouring molten iron into a mould, Athy Co-Operative Foundry, County Kildare

*Green sand moulding is a highly skilled craft. This image shows a timber pattern being removed from one half of a green sand mould
(Image courtesy of Historic Scotland and Charles Laing & Sons, Edinburgh)*

IDENTIFYING CAST IRON

Cast iron can only be shaped by pouring molten iron into a mould. Because moulds are usually made in two halves, it is often possible to find a mould line. This form of ironwork tends to have identical elements that show no variations from one to the other because a single pattern could be used to produce multiple castings. Flanges, slotted grooves and concealed bolts and pins are the most common methods of joining individual castings together. Cast ironwork tends to be made up of fewer parts than wrought iron because, where wrought iron needs many individually-shaped pieces to make up a whole design, a similar design in cast iron might only require one pattern. Cast iron manufacturers often included their company name on castings. These are frequently found at the base of columns or on flat surfaces of railings or finial bases.

This design is typical of cast iron panels cast in repeating, identical sections. Patterns for railings such as these had to be designed so that there were no undercuts – it had to be possible to pull the pattern out of the sand mould without pulling away any of the sand (which would get trapped behind undercuts) in the process. Some panels have a taper from one side to the other which aided the removal of the pattern from the sand mould

Cast iron railing panels were joined together by means of lugs and slotting systems such as the arrangement illustrated above

Ductile Iron

Ductile iron is a newer version of grey cast iron and is also known as 'spheroidal graphitic' or 'SG' iron. It is sometimes used as an alternative to grey cast iron due to its greater ductile strength when compared to grey cast iron. It was invented in 1942 by Keith Millis to overcome the brittle nature of grey cast iron. Ductile iron is used for car and machine parts, as well as for building fixings and structural materials.

Ductile iron is a common substitute for structural cast iron and, in some cases, wrought iron components and is widely available. Where there is the possibility of tensile stresses being placed on a cast iron member, ductile iron is often considered a good substitute because it is stronger in tension, although this is a contentious issue when dealing with historic ironwork. Little research has been conducted to determine the exact difference in tensile strength between ductile and grey cast iron. There is currently not enough understanding of these differences to warrant the use of ductile iron in place of grey cast iron in all cases. Although it is a form of iron, it is nevertheless a different metal to grey cast iron or wrought iron. In general, ductile iron should only be used in exceptional cases.

Pig Iron

Pig iron is a form of cast iron containing a high amount of carbon (up to 4%). It is the initial product of smelting iron ore in a blast furnace and was the earliest form of cast iron. However, its high carbon content makes it undesirably brittle and so further treatments were developed over time to reduce this brittleness and make it a more useful material. It was rarely used directly as a material itself. Instead, it was processed further in different ways to make wrought iron, cast iron and steel.

Ore was smelted in a blast furnace and the resulting metal – pig iron – was cast into ingots referred to as pigs. A long channel was dug out of sand in the foundry floor into which molten iron was poured directly from the furnace. This channel fed a series of moulds which ran off this channel to form the molten iron into ingots. It was thought that the channel and moulds resembled a sow suckling a litter of piglets, hence the moulds were called pigs. The pig iron was then treated in different ways to produce wrought iron, cast iron, or steel. Pig iron is still used in the production of steel and is referred to as hot metal.

Pure iron

Pure iron is produced by the steel-making industry to make special steels. It is a very pure form of iron which is homogenous in composition and low in carbon (0.004%). This low carbon content means that it is malleable and can be forged. Pure iron has good corrosion resistance although there is currently contention within the industry as to whether its corrosion resistance is equal to, better, or worse than that of wrought iron.

Pure iron is occasionally used by blacksmiths as a substitute for wrought iron in conservation projects and can be obtained from a single source in the UK. While the use of a substitute material is not ideal in conservation projects, wrought iron is often beyond the budget of private individuals. In these cases pure iron might be considered as an alternative to wrought iron. However, as it is a different material to wrought iron, the use of this material is not recommended for high-status wrought iron conservation projects.

Steel

Steel comes from the same raw source as iron (iron ore). It is an alloy of iron and other elements, most commonly carbon, and its properties have long been distinguished from those of iron. Wootz, a form of crucible steel, is believed to be one of the earliest forms of this metal and was first developed in India, probably in or around 300 AD. Until the mid-nineteenth century, steel was an expensive material that could not be produced on a large scale. It was not until the invention of the Bessemer process (named after its inventor Henry Bessemer) in 1856, that steel could be mass-produced. Bessemer had been attempting to find a new way of industrially producing wrought iron when he inadvertently discovered a method of mass-producing steel.

Nowadays, steel is produced by oxidising molten pig iron in a basic oxygen converter (BOS converter). The pig iron is taken directly from the blast furnace and poured into the BOS converter. Oxygen is then blown into the molten metal at supersonic speed. The resulting metal is taken to the casting plant where it is continuously cast (a conveyor-like process whereby the molten steel is gradually cooled as it passes along the conveyor) and finally passed into a rolling mill to be shaped.

Mild steel

There are various types of carbon steel ranging from low carbon steel (containing up to 0.15% carbon) and mild steel (0.15 – 0.25% carbon) to medium-carbon steels (0.25 – 0.5% carbon) and high carbon steels (0.5 – 1.5% carbon). Mild steel is a type of carbon steel, and contains both pure iron and carbon in the form of cementite. Both the iron and cementite in steel are electrically conductive so this can cause galvanic corrosion to occur when moisture is present. In other words, there is an in-built susceptibility to corrosion in mild steel. Mild steel is widely used today for construction and engineering projects.

Because wrought iron is only available in recycled form and is difficult to obtain, mild steel is commonly used as a substitute material. It is not an appropriate substitute; it does not look the same, nor does it behave in the same way. In addition to this, mild steel is considered by many to be more prone to corrosion than wrought iron.

IDENTIFYING MILD STEEL

Mild steel is often difficult to distinguish from wrought iron because it can be shaped and assembled using the same techniques. Invented in 1856, mild steel had almost entirely replaced wrought iron as a structural building material by the closing decades of the nineteenth century. Nevertheless, wrought iron remained popular for non-structural domestic ironwork such as railings, balconies and verandahs. In a historic context, mild steel is likely to be found in structural elements (such as beams), or in previous repair work to wrought iron items. Steel beams often have a manufacturer's name stamped or rolled onto their surface, which can also help in identifying the material.

Where decorative items such as gates and railings are concerned, mild steel is more often assembled by a fabricator using modern welding techniques and fixings than by a blacksmith using the traditional techniques associated with wrought iron. In many cases the quality and style of workmanship can be an indication of the material. Mild steel decorative features may be less finely worked and finished than similar wrought iron features. Mild steel scrolls in particular are often poorly shaped and lack the typical traditional taper in thickness and width from the root to the tip of the scroll. The surface of wrought iron has often been worked (for example, a blacksmith who did not have a bar in the required size would hammer it to the required dimension), and slight variations in thickness can sometimes be seen.

The original cast iron finial is depicted on top. Mild steel replacement finials are shown below. These are flat and poorly designed in comparison to the original and have been individually welded onto the rail

Stainless steel

Stainless steel was first developed in 1913 by Harry Brearley, head of the Firth-Brown research laboratories in Sheffield. Through testing, he discovered that steel containing certain proportions of chromium, carbon, and manganese had superior corrosion properties to other carbon steel samples he was testing. There are now many varieties of stainless steel which each have different properties.

Stainless steel is largely used for domestic products and the automotive industry, but is also used for construction. It is sometimes specified to replace wrought iron fixings and has also been used as a substitute for wrought iron flat bars on railings. Its use is preferable to mild steel because of its superior corrosion resistance and it is particularly well suited for use as screws and bolts. It can also be welded to wrought iron. Where stainless steel is used, it should be isolated from original wrought iron by using nylon or a similar inert material as a barrier between the two metals.

THE DIFFERENCES BETWEEN WROUGHT IRON, CAST IRON AND STEEL

Wrought iron, cast iron, and steel have distinct properties from one another, although each comes from the same raw material: iron ore. Iron ore is composed of the mineral (iron oxide), and gangue (basically everything else within the iron ore). The most commonly used types of ore are hematite (Fe_2O_3) and magnetite (Fe_3O_4).

One of the main factors that determine whether a metal is wrought iron, cast iron or steel is the quantity and type of carbon it contains. The level and type of carbon is affected by the methods used to smelt iron ore and treat the resulting extracted metal. As a general rule of thumb, wrought iron contains less than 0.2% carbon, steel generally contains between 0.06% and 2% carbon, and cast iron contains between 2% and 4% carbon. The carbon content affects the properties of iron and steel: their hardness, malleability and strength. The more carbon a metal contains the harder, and therefore more brittle, it becomes. So wrought iron, which has low carbon content, can be shaped by hammering. Cast iron, however, is hard and strong due to its higher carbon content, and cannot be hammered as it would shatter.

Aluminium

Aluminium is often used as a substitute for cast ironwork. Extracted from bauxite ore by a process of electrolysis and the application of heat, it is a widely available material. Aluminium is malleable and ductile (it can be pressed and machined to shape) and can also be cast. However, where it is placed beside cast iron it is likely to corrode sacrificially to the iron and at an accelerated rate. This process can easily be recognised by the white powdery corrosion material that develops on the surface of the aluminium. Aluminium has the added disadvantage that paint does not adhere well to its surface unless it has been etched before paint is applied.

Bronze

Bronze, an alloy of copper and tin, is sometimes used as an alternative to cast iron and is widely available. It can only be shaped by casting and can be cast in green sand moulds. Although bronze is a relatively stable metal, there is a risk of galvanic corrosion occurring if it is placed in direct contact with iron (although the risk is lower than placing iron in contact with aluminium or steel). Nevertheless, phosphor bronze fixings are a good alternative to stainless steel but should be isolated from the surrounding iron by nylon or a similar inert material to minimise the risk of galvanic corrosion.

Reinforced fibreglass

Reinforced fibreglass is not a metal but is sometimes proposed as a substitute material in repairs. It is strong, but is not historically authentic and should therefore only be used in exceptional circumstances where the original ironwork does not have a structural function. Fibreglass can also be used in some cases to hold cracked sections of ironwork together by attaching it to the reverse face of the iron.

8. Glossary

BACKSTAY

A backstay is an arm of iron that stabilises railings by running from the top rail into the ground.

BAR

A bar is a single shaft of metal placed vertically in a piece of ironwork.

BLACKSMITH

A blacksmith is a craftsperson who works with wrought iron and mild steel, and is capable of forging and fire welding. Traditionally blacksmiths made a wide range of products from agricultural equipment to architectural ironwork such as railings.

BRADDED / BRADDING

Also known as 'riveted' / 'riveting'. A bar of iron is slotted through another piece of iron and the end is hammered into a dome to secure it in place.

BRAZING

Brazing is a form of welding that uses an alloy rod, commonly brass or bronze, to join two sections of iron or steel together.

CAST IRON

Cast iron is a hard and brittle form of iron which is higher in carbon than wrought iron and crystalline in structure. It cannot be forged and can only be shaped by casting.

COLLAR

Cast iron collars are decorative cast elements that usually slot over wrought iron bars. Wrought iron collars are bands that fit around two or more elements of wrought ironwork to secure them together.

COPING STONE

A coping stone is a stone topping a wall.

COVER PLATE

Also known as a slam bar, this is a flat plate of wrought iron on the non-hinged side of a gate frame. It often prevents the gate from swinging beyond the gate post or adjoining leaf (in the case of a double-leafed gate).

FINIAL

A finial is a decorative element placed at the top of something, for example at the top of bars forming a length of railings. It can also refer to a decorative element placed on top of a roof, dormer window, ridge, or other portion of a roof. A finial placed on the highest point of a roof is called a terminal.

FIRE WELDING

Traditionally fire welding (also known as forge welding) was done by heating two pieces of iron and then hammering them together to form a seamless join.

FORGE

Verb: to shape using a hammer. Noun: the workshop of a blacksmith / the fire at which the blacksmith works.

FORGE WELDING

See 'fire welding'

FOUNDER

A founder is a craftsperson who works in a foundry and makes cast iron items.

FOUNDRY

A foundry is a workshop with a furnace where castings are made.

GUDGEON

Also known as a heel cup, a gudgeon is the hole that receives the pintle or heel of the gate so that it can swivel open and closed.

HEEL

A heel, or pintle, is the round-section foot or bar that projects from the base of the hinged side of a gate frame. It slots into the gudgeon and enables the gate to swing open and closed.

HEEL CUP

See 'gudgeon'

HUSK

A husk is made of cast iron, often in the shape of a bell-flower, nut-shell, or wheat ear. Similar to a cast iron collar but longer in length, it is an element that slots over bars to add decoration.

IRONWORKS

Traditionally an ironworks was where wrought iron was made and processed.

MORTICE-AND-TENON JOINT

The end of one piece is stepped to form a tongue (the tenon) which is narrower than the main body of iron. This tongue pierces through a corresponding hole (the mortice) in the second section of iron.

MOULD

A mould is a depression made in sand into which molten iron is poured to produce a casting. Moulds were traditionally made of green sand and were formed using a pattern to create the desired shape.

NEWEL

A newel is a vertical post usually used to anchor and stabilise railings or handrails. Newels are normally placed at intervals or key points along a run of railings or other ironwork.

PATTERN

A pattern is used in the making of cast iron. Patterns were traditionally carved in wood and were used to create the shaped depression in sand to form a mould into which molten iron would be poured.

PIG IRON

Pig iron is one of the crudest forms of iron. It is obtained from the first smelting of iron ore.

PINTLE

See 'heel'

PINNING

Pinning is a repair technique for holding sections of iron or steel together. Fractured sections can be joined together by drilling one or more threaded holes into each fractured face and screwing them together using a threaded or plain stainless steel bar.

PLATING

Plating is a repair method that uses a strap or plate of iron or steel to hold fractured sections together.

PURE IRON

Pure iron is homogenous in composition, low in carbon and without the slag content found in wrought iron. It is malleable, so can be forged.

RAIL

A rail is the horizontal (usually flat) member of a railing or gate, often pierced by vertical bars.

RIVET / RIVETING

See 'bradded / bradding'

SLAM BAR

see 'cover plate'

STEEL

Steel is an alloy of iron and carbon. It has a homogenous structure, is strong in tension and compression, but is generally considered to have lower corrosion resistance than iron.

STITCHING

Stitching is a repair method for holding sections of iron or steel together. One series of holes is drilled along the length of a fracture, and another series of holes is drilled perpendicular to the fracture. A series of metal keys are then inserted into the holes across the fracture to hold the sections of metal together.

WELDING

Traditionally fire welding was done by heating two pieces of iron and then hammering them together to form a seamless join. Modern welding uses a variety of techniques which involve melting a rod of metal into the joint to hold two sections of iron or steel together.

WROUGHT IRON

Wrought iron is a malleable form of iron that is low in carbon and contains strands of slag, which give it a fibrous composition. It cannot be shaped by casting and is usually shaped by forging.

Useful contacts

The conservation officer in the local authority should be the first person to contact with queries regarding a historic building. Other useful contacts include:

Architectural Heritage Advisory Unit, Department of the Environment, Heritage and Local Government
Telephone: (01) 888 2000
Web: www.environ.ie

Construction Industry Federation, Construction House, Canal Road, Dublin 6
Telephone: (01) 406 6000
Web: www.heritageregistration.ie

Heritage Council, Áras na hOidhreachta, Church Lane, Kilkenny, Co. Kilkenny
Telephone: (056) 777 0777
Web: www.heritagecouncil.ie

Irish Architectural Archive, 45 Merrion Square, Dublin 2
Telephone: (01) 663 3040
Web: www.iarc.ie

Irish Artist Blacksmiths Association
Telephone: (01) 462 2788

Irish Georgian Society, 74 Merrion Square, Dublin 2
Telephone: (01) 676 7053
Web: www.igs.ie

Royal Institute of the Architects of Ireland, 8 Merrion Square, Dublin 2
Telephone: (01) 676 1703
Web: www.riai.ie

Further reading

Ashurst, John; Ashurst, Nicola; Wallis, Geoff and Toner, Dennis, *Practical Building Conservation, Volume 4: Metals,* Aldershot: Gower Technical Press Ltd (1988)

English Heritage, English Heritage Research Transactions, *Metals,* Volume 1, London: James & James (1998)

Fearn, Jacqueline, *Cast Iron,* Buckinghamshire: Shire Publications Ltd (2001)

Glasgow West Conservation Trust, *Conservation Manual, Section 4: Ironwork,* Glasgow: Glasgow West Conservation Trust (1993)

Keohane, Frank, ed. *Period houses – a conservation guidance manual,* Dublin: Dublin Civic Trust (2001)

Hayman, Richard, *Wrought Iron,* Buckinghamshire: Shire Publications (2000)

Rynne, Colin, *Industrial Ireland 1750-1930, an archaeology,* Cork: The Collins Press (2006)

Swailes, T., Historic Scotland Practitioners Guide, *Scottish Iron Structures,* Edinburgh: Historic Scotland (2006)

Walker, Bruce and others, Historic Scotland TCRE Technical Advice Note, *Corrugated Iron and Other Ferrous Cladding,* Edinburgh: Historic Scotland (2004)